JEFF KINNEY'NİN DİĞER KİTAPLARI

Çeviri: Kenan Özgür

Wimpy Kid
SAFTİRİK
GREG'İN GÜNLÜĞÜ
AH KALBİM!

Jeff Kinney

epsilon®

SAFTİRİK GREG'İN GÜNLÜĞÜ AH KALBİM!

Orijinal Adı: Diary Of a Wimpy Kid / The Third Wheel
Yazarı: Jeff Kinney

Yayın Yönetmeni: Aslı Tunç
Çeviri: Kenan Özgür
Düzenleme: Gülen Işık
Düzelti: Fahrettin Levent
Kapak Uygulama: Berna Özbek Keleş

24. Baskı: Aralık 2018
ISBN: 978-9944-82-612-9

Kitap Tasarım: Jeff Kinney
Kapak Tasarım: Chad W. Beckerman ve Jeff Kinney
İngilizce ilk baskı: 2012 (Amulet Books - Imprint of Abrams)
Türkçe yayın hakkı © Epsilon Yayınevi Ticaret ve Sanayi A.Ş.

Baskı ve Cilt:
Vizyon Basımevi
Beylikdüzü O.S.B. Mah., Orkide Cad., No: 1/Z
Beylikdüzü/İstanbul
Tel: (212) 671 61 51 Faks: (212) 671 61 50
Sertifika No: 28640

Yayımlayan:
Epsilon Yayınevi Ticaret ve Sanayi A.Ş.
Osmanlı Sok., No: 18/4-5 Taksim/İstanbul
Tel: (212) 252 38 21 Faks: (212) 252 63 98
Internet adresi: www.epsilonyayinevi.com
e-mail: epsilon@epsilonyayinevi.com
Sertifika No: 34590

GRAM'A

OCAK

<u>Pazar</u>

Keşke günlük yazmaya çok daha önce başlasaymışım. Çünkü biyografimi yazacak olan kişinin, ortaokula başlamadan önceki hayatımla ilgili bir sürü sorusu olacak.

Neyse ki, doğduğumdan beri başıma gelen hemen her şeyi hatırlıyorum. Hatta DOĞMADAN ÖNCE başıma gelen şeyleri bile hatırlayabiliyorum.

O günlerde karanlıkta yüzüyor, taklalar atıyor ve ne zaman canım istese şekerleme yapıyordum.

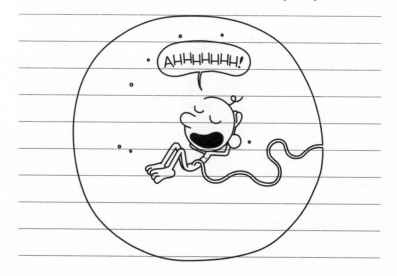

Sonra bir gün, çok tatlı bir uykunun tam ortasındayken, dışarıdan gelen garip seslerle uyandım.

O sırada duyduğum şeyin ne olduğunu anlayamadım ama sonra bunun annemin karnına dayadığı hoparlörlerle içeri verdiği müzik olduğunu fark ettim.

Sanırım annem ben doğmadan önce her gün bana klasik müzik çalarsa, bunun bir tür dahi olmamı sağlayacağını filan düşünüyordu.

Hoparlörlerin mikrofonu da vardı ve annem müzik çalmadığı zamanlarda, hayatında olup biten her şeyi anlatıyordu bana.

Babam işten eve döndüğünde de, annem bu kez ONUN gününün nasıl geçtiğine dair rapor verdiriyordu bana.

Hepsi bu kadar da değildi. Annem her gece yatmadan önce yarım saat bana kitap okuyordu.

Sorun, benim uyku düzenimin anneminkiyle uyuşmamasıydı. Bu yüzden annem uyurken, ben gözümü kırpmadan yatıyordum.

Ama keşke annem bana kitap okurken daha dikkatli dinleseymişim.

Geçen hafta okulda bir kitapla ilgili habersiz sınav olduk. Kitabı okumamıştım. Doğmadan önce annemin bana okuduğundan emindim ama ayrıntıların hiçbirini hatırlayamıyordum.

Herhalde annemin o kitabı okuduğum hafta, ben başka bir şeyler yapmakla meşguldüm.

İşin acayip yanı, annemin sesini bana duyurmak için mikrofon kullanmasına GEREK YOKTU.

Yani, ben zaten onun İÇİNDEYDİM.
Söylediği her sözcüğü istesem de istemesem de
duyabiliyordum.

Ayrıca dışarıda olup biten hemen HER ŞEYİ
de duyabiliyordum. Yani, annemle babam
romantikleştiklerinde, BUNU da dinlemek
zorunda kalıyordum.

İnsanlar etrafımda birbirlerine sevgi gösterisi yaparken kendimi rahat hissetmemişimdir oldum bittim. HELE bunu yapanlar annemle babamsa. Onları durdurmaya çalışıyordum ama mesajı bir türlü almıyorlardı.

Hatta başvurduğum her yol işleri DAHA DA BETER hale getiriyordu sanki.

Birkaç ay böyle yaşadıktan sonra, kendimi oradan çıkmak zorunda hissettim ve işte bu yüzden üç hafta erken doğdum. Ama doğum odasının buz gibi havası ve insanın gözünü kör eden ışıklarıyla karşılaşınca, çıktığıma pişman oldum. Keşke biraz daha içeride kalsaymışım.

Dünyaya geldiğimde çok uykusuz ve keyifsizdim. Moralim bozuktu. Bu yüzden, bundan sonra yeni doğan bir bebeğin resmini gördüğünüzde, neden o kadar suratsız göründüğünü anlarsınız artık.

İşte yeni küçük
sevinç yumağımız

Gregory Heffley

2 kilo
400 gram

Gerçi HÂLÂ tam olarak uykumu almış değilim ve inanın bana, bunun için elimden geleni yapıyorum.

Doğduğumdan beri, karanlıkta, mutluluk içinde yüzerken yaşadığım o duyguyu yeniden yaşamaya çalışıyorum.

Ama dört insanla birlikte aynı evde yaşıyorsanız, mutlaka bir münasebetsiz gelir ve bütün keyfinizi kaçırır.

Ağabeyim Rodrick ile doğduktan birkaç gün sonra tanıştım. O zamana kadar tek çocuk olduğumu sanıyordum. Öyle olmadığımı öğrenince, büyük hayal kırıklığına uğradım.

Ailem o zamanlar çok küçük bir evde oturuyordu. Ben de odamı Rodrick ile paylaşmak zorundaydım. Bebek karyolasında Rodrick yatıyordu, bu yüzden hayatımın ilk birkaç ayı boyunca, şifoniyerin en üst çekmesinde uyumak zorunda kaldım. Bunun yasal bile olmadığından eminim.

Sonra babam iş malzemelerini çalışma odası olarak kullandığı odadan çıkardı ve burayı çocuk odasına dönüştürdü. Rodrick'in eski karyolası bana verildi, ona da yeni bir yatak alındı.

O günlerde sahip olduğum HEMEN HER ŞEY Rodrick'in eskileriydi.

Bana gelen bütün eşyalar ya eski püskü ve yıpranmış ya da salya kaplı oluyordu.

EMZİĞİM bile Rodrick'ten kalmaydı. Sanırım Rodrick henüz emziği bana vermeye hazır değildi. Bence bu, beni hiçbir zaman sevmemesinin nedenini açıklıyor.

Uzun bir süre evde dört kişi yaşadık. Sonra annem bir gün bana bir bebeğinin daha olacağını söyledi. Beni önceden uyarmasına memnun oldum, böylece kendimi hazırlayacaktım.

Küçük kardeşim Manny geldiğinde, herkes onun çok şeker olduğunu düşündü. Ama bebeklerle ilgili size söylemedikleri bir şey var: Yeni doğan bebeklerde, karında, göbek bağının kesildiği yerde siyah bir kordon oluyor.

Zaman içinde bu kordon kuruyup düşüyor ve bebek normal görünen bir göbek deliğine sahip oluyor. Mesele şu: Manny'nin göbek kordonunu kimse bulamadı. Ben de bugün bile hâlâ kordonun bir yerde karşıma çıkacağını düşünüp paranoya yapıyorum.

Ben yeni doğduğumda, annem her gün beni bir saat boyunca televizyonun karşısına oturtur ve eğitici videolar izletirdi.

Bu videolar daha akıllı ve zeki olmamı sağladı mı bilmiyorum ama en azından videoya izlemek İSTEDİĞİM bir şey koymayı öğrenecek kadar akıllıydım.

AYNI ZAMANDA uzaktan kumandanın pillerini çıkarmayı da öğrendim, böylece kimse eğitici videoları tekrar açamıyordu.

Ama bebekken etrafta pek fazla dolaşamıyorsunuz, bu yüzden pilleri saklayabileceğim tek bir yer vardı.

Bence annem ben küçükken yerde daha fazla emeklememe izin vermeliydi çünkü fiziksel konularda oyun grubumdaki diğer çocuklara göre ÇOK geriydim. Diğerleri otururken ve kanepede gezinirken, ben hâlâ kafamı yerden kaldırmaya çalışıyordum.

Sonra bir gün annem bana "Bebekler İçin Macera Yürüteci" denen şeyi aldı. Rodrick'ten bana kalmayan tek şeydi bu.

Macera Yürüteci MÜTHİŞTİ. Üzerinde kendi kendini eğlendirebileceğin bir milyon zamazingo ve bir de fincan koyma yeri vardı.

Ama en güzel tarafı, gitmek istediğim her yere YÜRÜMEK zorunda kalmadan ulaşmamı sağlamasıydı.

Ne zaman Bebekler için Macera Yürüteci'me binsem, oyun grubumdaki bütün arkadaşlarımın kendilerini salak gibi hissettiklerini anlayabiliyordum.

Ama annem bir çocuk bakımı dergisinde yürüteç kullanmanın iyi bir fikir olmadığını, çünkü çocukların kendi başlarına yürümeleri için doğru kasların gelişmesini engellediğini okudu. Bunun üzerine yürüteci mağazaya iade etti. Ben de eskiye döndüm.

Biraz uzun zaman aldı ama sonunda yürümeyi ÖĞRENDİM. Sonra, ne olduğunu anlamadan, kendimi kreşte buldum.

Annemin çaldığı klasik müzikler ve izlettiği eğitici DVD'ler yüzünden diğer çocuklara fark atacağımı umuyordum. Ama diğer anneler de aynı şeyleri yapmış olmalı ki, kreşteki rekabet çok sıkıydı.

Yani, ben daha ancak bir yetişkinin yardımı olmadan eldivenlerimi çıkarabilirken, düğme ve fermuar kullanmayı bilen çocuklar vardı.

Sınıf arkadaşlarımın bazıları kendi adını yazabiliyordu. Bir ya da iki kişi de elliye kadar sayabiliyordu.

Onlara yetişemeyeceğimi biliyordum. Ben de herkese yanlış bilgiler vererek onları geriletmeye karar verdim.

Ama planım ters tepti çünkü kreş öğretmenim anneme benim renkleri ve şekilleri diğer çocuklar gibi öğrenemediğimi söyledi. Ancak annem de benim akıllı olduğumu ve sorunun belki de yeterince ZORLANMAMAM olduğunu söyledi.

Bunun üzerine annem beni kreşten aldı ve bir sınıf ATLATARAK anaokuluna verdi. Ancak bu karar tam bir felaketti.

Anaokulundaki çocuklar bana DEV gibi görünüyorlardı. Makasla kesmeyi ya da çizgilerin arasını boyamayı filan da becerebiliyorlardı.

Daha anaokulunda bir tam gün bile geçirmemiştim ki öğretmen annemi arayarak gelip beni almasını söylemek zorunda kaldı.

Ertesi gün annem beni tekrar kreşe götürdü ve öğretmene beni geri alıp alamayacağını sordu. Umarım okul kayıtları insanı gittiği her yerde takip etmiyordur çünkü insanlar benim anaokulundan atıldığımı öğrenirlerse, iyi bir iş bulmam zor olabilir.

<u>Pazartesi</u>

Annemin, küçükken benim üzerimde denediklerinin işe yaramadığına karar verdiğinden eminim. Çünkü Manny'ye karşı tamamen farklı bir yaklaşım sergiliyor.

Bir kere, annem Manny'nin canı ne isterse onu izlemesine izin veriyor. Manny de günde yirmi dört saat "Dıgıllar" adlı programı izliyor.

Ben de birkaç kez "Dıgıllar"ı izlemeyi denedim ama neler olup bittiğini HİÇ anlamadım. Sanırım Dıgılların yalnızca üç yaşındakilerin anlayabileceği kendilerine özgü bir dilleri var.

Manny programı izledikten sonra, ailemizden kimse onu anlamayınca çok öfkeleniyor.

Ancak geçen gün annem gazetede "Dıgıllar"ın çocukların dil gelişiminde bir yıl kadar geride kalmalarına neden olduğunu, ayrıca onların sosyal becerilerine de zarar verdiğini söyleyen bir yazı okudu.

Eh, bu da çok şeyi açıklıyor. Manny'nin hiç gerçek arkadaşı yok. Annem ne zaman evde bir oyun grubu toplasa, diğer çocuklarla etkileşim kurmayan tek çocuk da Manny oluyor.

Bence bunun nedenlerinden biri, Manny'nin oyuncaklarını paylaşmayı sevmemesi. Bu yüzden eve çocuklar geldiğinde, Manny kendini yaşlı köpeğimizin oyun evine kapatıyor ve bütün oyuncaklarını kendine saklıyor.

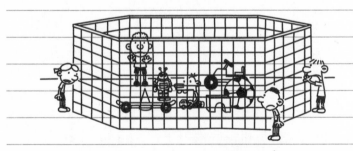

Annem ne zaman Manny'yi KENDİ KENDİNE diğer çocuklarla oynamaya ikna etmeye çalışsa, ters tepiyor.

Kilisede yeni bir uygulama başlattılar. Küçük çocukları ayin sırasında boyama yapıp oyun oynamaları için bodrum katına gönderiyorlar. Ama annem Manny'yi ilk kez aşağı indirdiğinde, oyun alanında yalnızca bir tane çocuk varmış ve o da Manny'ye vampir olduğunu söylemiş.

Manny için biraz üzüldüm aslında çünkü ben de onun yaşındayken korkunç bir çocukla uğraşmak zorunda kalmıştım. Anaokulunda Bradley adında bir çocuk vardı ve her fırsatta beni korkutuyordu.

Her gün eve geldiğimde anneme Bradley'yi anlatıyor ve artık okula gitmek istemediğimi söylüyordum. Ama o yaz Bradley ve ailesi başka bir yere taşındılar ve böylece sorun kendiliğinden halloldu.

Bradley taşındıktan sonra, annem sürekli yaramazlık yapan bir çocuğu anlatan "Kötü Bradley" adında bir öykü yazdı. Bradley gerçek hayatta kötü bir çocuktu ama annemin öyküsünde şeytanın ta kendisiydi.

Sanırım annem elinden geleni yapacak ve öyküsünü yayınlatacaktı ama Bradley ve ailesi ertesi bahar mahallemize geri döndüler. Annem de öyküyü yırtıp atmak zorunda kaldı.

Annem Kötü Bradley öyküsünü hiç yayınlatamasa da, bunu Manny'ye anaokulunda nasıl davranması gerektiğini öğretmek için kullandı. Bence Manny'nin kendi yaşındaki diğer çocuklardan korkmasının nedenlerinden biri de bu.

Manny'nin GERÇEK arkadaşları olmayabilir ama bir sürü HAYALİ arkadaşı var. Sayısını unuttum ama hatırladığım isimler şunlar: Joey, Petey, Danny, Charles Tribble, Diğer Charles Tribble, Küçük Jim ve Johnny Çedar.

Manny bu kadar çok arkadaşı nasıl uydurdu bilmiyorum ama inanın bana hepsini GERÇEK sanıyor. Bir keresinde bütün hayali arkadaşlarını markete götürdü ve annem güya Charles Tribble'ı dondurulmuş yiyecekler reyonunda unutunca, tam bir çöküş yaşadı.

Bazen, Manny bu hayali arkadaşları yemekten sonra fazladan tatlı yiyebilmek için filan mı uydurdu acaba, diye düşünüyorum.

Annem, Manny'ye hayali arkadaşlarının gerçek olmadığını söylersek, onun "travma" yaşayabileceğini söylüyor. Biz de böyle idare etmek zorunda kalıyoruz.

Umarım Manny bundan bir an önce kurtulur çünkü iş iyice saçma bir hal almaya başladı. Bazen, tuvalete girebilmek için, Manny'nin hayali arkadaşlarının işlerini bitirip çıkmalarını beklemek zorunda kalıyorum.

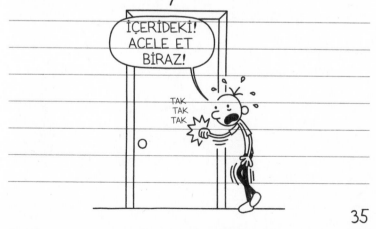

Son zamanlarda Manny bütün suçlarını hayali arkadaşlarının üzerine atmaya başladı. Geçen gün bir tabağı yere attı, sonra da anneme bunu grubun baş belası gibi görünen Johnny Çedar'ın yaptığını söyledi.

Annem de tabağı kırdığı ve sonra da yalan söylediği için Manny'yi cezalandırmak yerine, Johnny Çedar'a ceza verdi. İşin kötü yanı, ceza koltuğu, bizim salondaki yepyeni televizyon koltuğuydu. Bu yüzden ben, televizyon izlerken o koltuğa oturamadım.

Dediğim gibi, ben bu hayali arkadaş meselesinin tam bir saçmalık olduğunu biliyorum ama Manny bu konuda öyle ciddi davranıyor ki insanın inanası geliyor. Ne zaman evde bir yere oturacak olsam, Manny'nin arkadaşlarından hiçbirinin ortalıkta olmadığından emin oluyorum.

Yapmam gereken en son şey, televizyon izlemek için kendimi kanepeye atmak ve Küçük Jim'i ezmek.

Gerçi bugünlerde pek televizyon izlediğim de yok. Annem Manny ve onun sosyal becerileri konusunda o kadar endişeleniyor ki, Manny etraftayken televizyonun açık olmasını istemiyor.

Geçenlerde annem "Aile Gecesi" diye bir şey icat etti. Televizyon izlemek yerine hep birlikte oyun oynayacakmışız ya da yemeğe filan çıkacakmışız.

Sanırım amaç birbirimizle etkileşim kurmamızı sağlamak ve Manny'yi oyalamak.

Yemeğe çıktığımızda, genellikle kendimizi Corny Aile Restoranı'nda buluyoruz. Corny'nin kuralı var, kravat takmak yasak. Oraya ilk gittiğimizde babam bu kuralı biraz zor yollarla öğrendi.

Corny'de farklı oturma bölmeleri var. Ama bizim yanımızda hep Manny olduğu için, bizi "Çocukların Sokağı" denen aile bölmesinde oturtuyorlar.

Çocukların Sokağı'nda, bir aile kalkıp yerine başka bir aile oturmadan önce masayı ve ortalığı temizleme zahmetine bile katlanmıyorlar bence. Bu yüzden masanıza oturduğunuzda, yerde buruşturulup atılmış peçeteler, koltuklarda da yarısı yenmiş patates kızartmaları ile karşılaşıyorsunuz.

Corny'ye ilk gittiğimizde, koltuğuma bakmamıştım; üstü açık, fıstık ezmeli ve reçelli bir sandviçin üzerine oturmuşum.

Çocukların Sokağı'nın nefret ettiğim taraflarından biri de, tuvaletlerin hemen yanında olması. Tuvaletin kapıları ardına kadar açılıyor ve yemeğinizi yemeye çalışırken içeride olup bitenleri görebiliyorsunuz.

Corny'de servis de çok kötü; biz de açık büfeyi tercih edip kendi yemeğimizi kendimiz alıyoruz. Yemekler metal tepsilerde servis ediliyor ve hep bir tepsiye başka bir tepsinin yiyeceklerinden karışmış oluyor.

Tatlı bölümünde, kendi soslu dondurmanızı yapabileceğiniz bir dondurma köşesi var. Bunun kulağa harika geldiğini biliyorum ama çoğu restoranın müşterilerin makineleri kendi başlarına kullanmalarına izin vermemesinin bir nedeni var.

Annemin Corny'ye gitmek istemesinin nedenlerinden biri burada bir top havuzunun olması ve annemin de Manny'nin kendi yaşıtı çocuklarla oynamayı öğrenmesini ummasi.

Ancak Manny diğer çocuklardan saklanmak için kendini bir top yığınının altına gömüyor ve sonra da eve gitme vakti gelene kadar öylece bekliyor.

Geçen Perşembe Corny'ye gittik. Annem, Manny'nin top havuzunda saklanmasını önlemek için onun plastik tüplerin içine girmesini sağladı. Ama Manny orada çılgına döndü ve korkudan kendi başına aşağı inemedi.

Bunun üzerine annem bana oraya çıkıp Manny'yi aşağı indirmem gerektiğini söyledi. Çünkü ailede emekleyerek o tüplerin içine girebilecek kadar küçük olan tek kişi bendim.

Manny'nin tüplere girmek için kullandığı alanın içinden geçmek istedim ama çok sıkıştığım için gerisin geri çıkmak zorunda kaldım.

Bu durumda, Manny'ye ulaşmamın tek yolu, top havuzuna inen spiral plastik kaydırağa tırmanmaktı. Karanlık yerleri hiç sevmem, bunu yapmak da hiç hoşuma gitmemişti.

Üzerime gelen kimse olmadığından emin olmak için seslendim ama çocuklar beni duymazdan geldiler ve kaymaya devam ettiler.

AAAH! Trafik kargaşasını geçip tepeye vardığımda, Manny'yi bulmak için tüpler labirentinde sürünmeye başladım. İçeride havalandırma yoktu ve leş gibi kirli çorap kokuyordu.

Manny'yi aramak konusunda yanlış kişi olduğumu fark ettim çünkü labirentler konusunda hep kötü olmuşumdur. Bu sonbaharda annemle Reynold'in Çiftliği'ne gittik; annem çıkış yolunu bulmak konusunda bana güveniyordu.

Ama ben yolu öyle bir kaybettim ki annem gelip bizi kurtarmaları için yardım çağırmak zorunda kaldı.

Bu defa yanımda dışarı çıkmamı sağlayacak annemin cep telefonu da yoktu. Derken çocuklardan biri tünelin bir ucunda kusunca, bütün çocuklar kaydıraktan kaymak için benim tarafıma doğru koşmaya başladılar.

Sonunda Manny'yi tünellerden birinde buldum; ama o sırada artık bayılmak üzereydim. Bu yüzden garsonlardan biri kaydırağa tırmanıp Manny'yi VE beni kurtarmak zorunda kaldı.

Bu olayın en kötü tarafı en sevdiğim kot pantolonumu atmak zorunda kalmam oldu; çünkü pantolonu üç kez çamaşır suyuyla yıkadığım halde ayak kokusundan kurtaramadım.

Cumartesi
Bu sabah 6:30'da uyandım ve bir daha da uyuyamadım; çok sinir bozucuydu. Ama yılın başından beri bu sık sık başıma geliyor.

Yeni yıl günü annem Manny'nin gece yarısı uyanık olmanın nasıl bir şey olduğunu hissetmesini istedi; ama bunu Manny'yi o kadar geç saate kadar uyanık tutmadan yapacaktı. Bu yüzden evdeki saatleri üç saat geriye aldı.

Ancak bunu BANA söylemedi. Bu yüzden annemle babam Manny ile birlikte geriye sayarlarken, ben de vaktin GERÇEKTEN gece yarısı olduğunu düşündüm.

O gece saatin sabaha karşı 1:30 olduğunu zannederek saat 10:30'da yattım. Bu yüzden bu yıl bütün programım üç saat ileri oldu.

Hafta sonları genellikle babam beni yataktan sürükleyerek kaldırana kadar uyanmam. ÖZELLİKLE kışın, dışarısı buz gibiyken, yorganların altı sıcacık ve çok güzeldir.

Geçen kış bir cumartesi günü babamın saat 8:00'de beni uyandırıp yoldaki karları kürememi söylediğini hatırlıyorum.

Çok güzel bir rüyanın ortasındaydım ama yataktan kalkmayı, karları küremeyi ve sonra hemen yatağıma dönüp bir saniyesini bile kaçırmadan rüyama devam etmeyi başarmıştım.

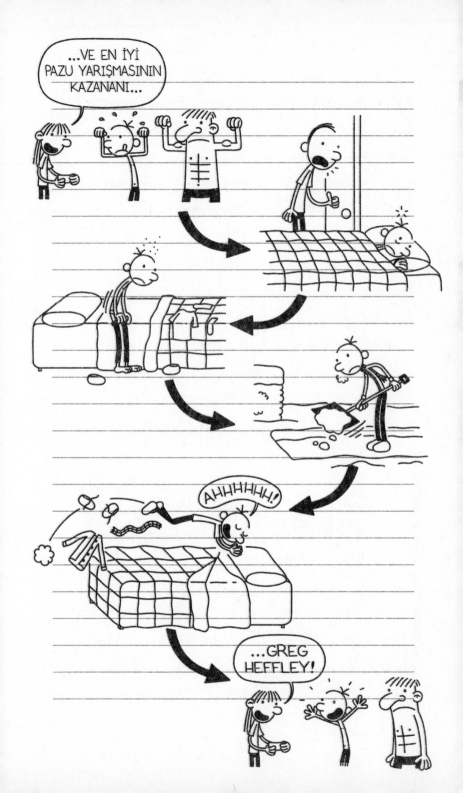

Bu sabah uyandıktan sonra, bir süre yatakta yatmaya devam edip yeniden uyumaya çalıştım. Sonunda aşağı inip kendime kahvaltı hazırladım. Cumartesi sabahı saat 8:00'den önce televizyonda güzel bir şey olmuyor; bu yüzden ev işlerinin bazılarını halletmeye karar verdim.

Rodrick ve benim hiçbir zaman bir şey almaya yetecek paramız olmuyor; bu yüzden annem ev işlerini yapmamız karşılığında bize harçlık veriyor. Benim işlerimden biri yemek odasındaki mobilyaların tozunu almak. O sabah tam bunu yapıyordum ki kapının vurulduğunu duydum.

Kapıyı açtım ve eşikte Gary Amca'yı görünce çok şaşırdım.

50

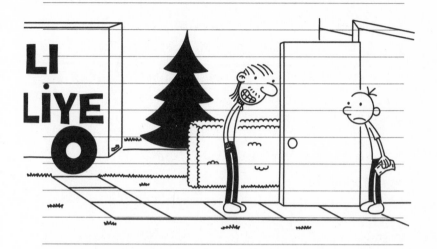

Bir dakika sonra babam aşağı indi ve kardeşini gördüğüne pek sevinmiş görünmedi.

Birkaç hafta önce, Gary Amca babamı aradı, "İnsanın karşısına hayatta bir kere çıkacak" bir iş fırsatıyla karşı karşıya olduğunu ve borç paraya ihtiyaç duyduğunu söyledi.

Babam, Gary Amca'ya para vermek istemedi çünkü Gary Amca insanlara borçlarını ödemek konusunda pek iyi bir şöhrete sahip değil.

Ama annem, babama bunu yapması gerektiğini, çünkü Gary Amca'nın onun kardeşi olduğunu, aile bireylerinin her zaman birbirlerine yardım etmeleri gerektiğini söyledi. Annem, Rodrick ile bana da hep böyle şeyler söyler. Umarım asla böbreğe falan ihtiyacım olmaz; çünkü eğer böyle bir durumda güveneceğim kişi Rodrick ise, başım dertte demektir.

Babam Gary Amca'ya parayı gönderdi ve bugüne kadar ondan hiç haber alamadık. Bugün Gary Amca eve girince bize olanları anlattı.

Boston'da caddede bir köşede tişört satan bir adamla tanışmış. Bu adam ona eğer işini devralmak isterse, kendisine yardımcı olabileceğini söylemiş.

Amcam, babamdan parayı aldıktan sonra,
adamın tişörtlerini satın almış. Ama Gary
Amca, tişörtlerin üzerinde bir yazı olduğunu
bilmiyormuş. Sorunu fark ettiğinde, adam
çoktan ortadan kaybolmuş.

Gary Amca, babama yeniden kendi ayakları
üzerinde durana kadar kalacak bir yere ihtiyacı
olduğunu söylediğinde, babam buna pek memnun
olmadı. Ancak sonra annem aşağı indi ve Gary
Amca'ya evimizde istediği kadar kalabileceğini
söyledi.

Ancak annem yolda nakliye kamyonunu görünce, Gary Amca'ya evimizde fazladan mobilya için hiç yer olmadığını söylemek zorunda kaldı.

Gary Amca anneme endişelenmesine gerek olmadığını, çünkü kendisinin hiç mobilyasının OLMADIĞINI söyledi. Nakliye kamyonu kutu kutu tişörtlerle doluydu. Sabahın geri kalanını bunları garajımıza yerleştirerek geçirdik.

Gary Amca'nın bunları satmak konusunda pes ettiğini hiç sanmıyorum. Birini üç papel karşılığında Rodrick'e kakaladı. Rodrick beleşe konduğunu sanıyor galiba.

Pazartesi

Gary Amca ile yaşamak hiç kolay değil. Evdeki ilk birkaç gecesinde Manny'nin odasında şişme yatakta uyudu. Ancak Gary Amca, gece yarısı uyanmasına neden olan kabuslar görüyor. Geçen pazartesi de çok kötü bir kabus görmüş.

Bu yüzden artık Gary Amca oturma odasındaki kanepede uyuyor. Manny'nin yatağı da duvarlardan uzak olsun diye odanın ortasına çekildi.

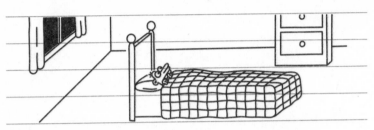

Gary Amca'nın kanepemizde uyuması çok rahatsız edici. Kendisi bütün gece kötü rüyalar görüyor, sonra da günün büyük bölümünü uyuyarak geçiriyor. Okuldan sonra biraz rahatlamak ve televizyon seyretmek isterken, bu durum insanın çok sinirini bozuyor.

Gary Amca'dan en çok etkilenen kişi RODRİCK ama.

Gary Amca bize taşınmadan önce, Rodrick hayatını, özellikle hafta sonlarını oturma odasındaki kanepede geçiriyordu.

Artık Rodrick'in, cumartesi sabahları babam onu bodrumdaki yatağından zorla kaldırdığında gidecek hiçbir yeri yok.

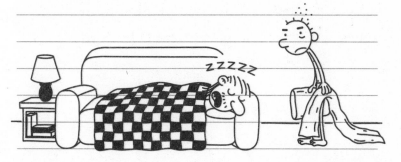

Geçen gün Rodrick üst kata çıktı ve Gary Amca'yı kendi yerinde görünce, o da kanepenin başka bir kısmında uyumaya devam etti.

Babam, kendisine bir iş bulması konusunda Gary Amca'nın başının etini yiyor ama Gary Amca denediğini ve kimsenin onu işe almadığını söylüyor.

Gary Amca hiçbir işte birkaç günden uzun süre kalamadı. Son olarak yazın biber gazı üreten bir şirkette denek olarak çalıştı, daha öğle tatili gelmeden istifa ettiğinden eminim.

Babam, Gary Amca'nın KENDİSİNİNKİ gibi bir iş bulmasını, yani bir ofiste düzenli saatler içinde çalışmasını istiyor.

Ama ben ofis işinin Gary Amca'ya göre olduğunu sanmıyorum. Bana göre olduğundan da emin değilim. Babam her gün işe giderken gömlek giyip kravat takmak zorunda. Takım elbiseye uygun ayakkabı ve çoraplar da giymesi gerekiyor.

Ben kararımı çoktan verdim. Büyüdüğümde, dizlerine kadar çıkan çoraplar giymenin gerekmediği bir iş bulacam.

Geçen yaz babam beni ofisindeki "Çocuğunu İşe Getir Günü"ne götürdü. Ancak işyerindeki insanlar işlerinin çocuklara sıkıcı geleceğini düşünmüş olmalılar ki yanlarında bir sürü eğlence malzemesi getirmişlerdi.

Günün büyük bölümünde, büyükler ofislerinde işlerini yaparlarken biz çocuklar kafeteryada kaldık.

Günün sonuna doğru, babam beni ofisine götürdü. Önemli bir projeyi tamamlamaya çalışıyordu. Ben de onun yanına oturup bekledim. Ama sanırım biri onun omzunun üzerinden bakarken konsantre olması zordu.

Babam, gidip abur cubur makinesinden kendime bir şeyler almam için bana para verdi. Galiba bir süreliğine benden kurtulmaya çalışıyordu. Bu yüzden, ben bir dakika sonra elimde bir paket mısır cipsiyle dönünce pek de mutlu olmadı.

Babam bana gerçekten elindeki işi bitirmek zorunda olduğunu ve kendisi işlerini hallederken benim de gidip oturacak başka bir yer bulmamı söyledi. O gün kafası gerçekten dağınık olmalı ki, eve gitti ve beni unuttu! Eğer temizlik görevlisi beni bulmasaydı, bütün gece oraya tıkılıp kalabilirdim.

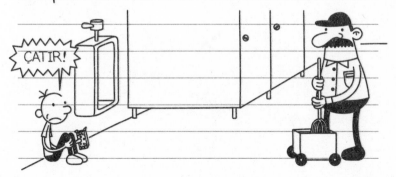

Her neyse, babam, Gary Amca'nın hiç parasının olmamasından ve sürekli kendisinden para tırtıklamasından çok rahatsız. Annem de, Gary Amca'ya harçlık vermeye başladı, üstelik onu ev işi yapmak zorunda bırakmadan! Bu bana çok yanlış geliyor.

Umarım Gary Amca, harçlığının bir kısmını kendine duş köpüğü almak için kullanır. Buraya geldiğinin ikinci günü, benim bütün köpüğümü kullandı. Su kristal gibi berrak olduğunda, banyo yapmak hiç de keyifli olmuyor!

<u>Salı</u>

Keşke birkaç hafta önce kot pantolonumu
atmak zorunda kalmasaydım çünkü bugün okulda
çok fiyakalı olmam gerekiyordu. Beden Eğitimi
dersinde salon danslarına başlıyormuşuz. Bayan
Moretta, hepimizin birer eş bulmamız gerektiğini
söyledi.

Bu yüzden okula boyu birkaç santim kısa gelen
kadife pantolonla gitmek için pek iyi bir gün
değildi.

AMAN BE
AMAN BE
AMAN BE

Bayan Moretta, birlikte dans etmek istediğimiz
kişinin adını küçük bir kâğıda yazarak eşlerimizi
seçeceğimizi söyledi. Kendisi kâğıtlara bakacak
ve bizi olabilecek en iyi şekilde eşleştirecekti.
<u>GEÇEN</u> yıl da modern dans dersleri için aynı
sistemi kullanmıştı ve ben yanmıştım.

Kâğıda sınıfımızın en güzel kızı Baylee Anthony'nin adını yazmıştım.

BAYLEE
ANTHONY

Ama o benim adımı yazmamış. Sınıftaki bütün diğer kızlar gibi, Bryce Anderson'ın adını yazmış. Bryce, McKenzie Pollard'ı seçti. Bayan Moretta da, ben Baylee'yi seçmiş olduğum için onu benim eşim yaptı.

Önce, Baylee eşim olduğu için çok heyecanlandım. Ama sonra üç hafta boyunca aynı saçmalıkla uğraşmak zorunda kaldım.

BEN ONU SEÇMEDİM.

Sanırım Baylee de bu yıl aynı şeyin tekrarlanmasını istemedi. Bunu anladım çünkü bugün kendisiyle dans etmek konusunda hiç şansının olmadığını düşünen bütün oğlanların yanına gitti ve dedi ki:

> EZİKLER, BİRİNİZ BENİM ADIMI YAZMAK İSTER MİSİNİZ?

Doğrusunu söylemem gerekirse, Ruby Bird ile eşleşmeyeyim de, kiminle eşleşirsem eşleşeyim, umurumda değil.

RUBY BIRD

Bildiğim kadarıyla, Ruby bugüne kadar okuldan uzaklaştırma cezası alan tek kız; nedeni de bir öğretmeni ısırması.

Hatta, Ruby'nin önde tek bir dişinin olmasının nedeni, diğer dişinin Bay Underwood'un kolunda kalması.

Ruby ile ne zaman koridorda karşılaşsam, ona iyi davranmaya çalışıyorum çünkü beni korkutuyor.

Ama bugün ona karşı FAZLA iyi olduğumu, kendisinden HOŞLANDIĞIMI sanabileceğini düşünüp endişelendim. İhtiyacım olan son şey, Ruby'nin benim adımı kâğıda yazması. Çünkü eğer benim danstaki eşim olursa, eninde sonunda mutlaka onu delirtecek BİR ŞEY yaparım ve diğer dişi de BENİM kolumda kalır.

Bu yüzden kâğıdımı bu olasılığın ortadan kalkması için kullandım.

> Lütfen beni
> Ruby Bird ile eşleştirmeyin.
> Saygılarımla, Greg Heffley

Bayan Moretta'nın bana kıyak yapması için, daha sonra yemek üzere sakladığım yarısı yenmiş şekerimi de feda ettim.

Çarşamba
Dün gece, Ruby'nin benim dans eşim olmaması için bol bol dua ettim.

Sonra birden bir endişeye kapıldım. Belki de insan ömrü boyunca belli sayıda duasına karşılık alıyordur ve ben de haklarımı çok hızlı yakıyorumdur. İleride bir gün, sırf sınırsız hakkım varmış gibi davrandığım için geriye hiç hakkımın kalmadığını öğrenirsem çok bozulurum.

Sanırım bu konuda daha dikkatli olmam gerek. Bu hafta sonu üst kattaki tuvalet tıkandı. Ben de tesisatçının, sorunu hallettikten sonra tuvaleti kullanmaması için dua ettim.

Bu arada söyleyeyim; dualarım konusunda başarı oranım yaklaşık %75. Bunun iyi mi yoksa kötü mü olduğunu bilmiyorum ama bir şeyden eminim. Ne kadar çok istersem isteyeyim, doğum günümde lazer kılıç alınmayacak bana.

Her neyse... Bundan sonra bir şey için dua ederken çok daha net olacağım çünkü bugün Beden Eğitimi dersinde duam kabul oldu; ama sonra yaşananlardan pek hoşnut olduğum söylenemez.

Dersin başında, Bayan Moretta dansta eş olanların isimlerini açıkladı. Sıra Ruby Bird'e geldiğinde nefesimi tuttum.

Ama Ruby, Fregley ile eşleşti. Bence tencere yuvarlandı, kapağını buldu! Bundan daha uyumlu bir çift olamazdı.

Sonunda, Bayan Moretta son kızın adını okudu. Geriye, aralarında benim de bulunduğum bir grup oğlan kalmıştı. Bu yıl sınıfımdaki oğlanların sayısı kızlardan çok daha fazla. Bu yüzden herkesin bir eşinin olmaması mantıklıydı.

Yine de o kâğıtlardan birine kimse benim adımı yazmadı diye biraz hayal kırıklığına uğramıştım.

Derken, geriye kalanlar olarak bizim salon dansları derslerine katılmak zorunda olmadığımızı, üç hafta boyunca spor salonunun diğer ucunda top oynayabileceğimizi fark ettik.

Ama biraz erken kutlama yapmışız. Bayan Moretta, HERKESİN dans etmek zorunda olduğunu söyledi ve biz oğlanları BİRBİRİMİZLE eşleştirmeye başladı. Biraz sonra kendimi Carlos Escalara ile dans ederken buldum!

Pazartesi

Bugün okulda Beden Eğitimi dersi iptal edildi çünkü dördüncü derste genel toplantı vardı. Bunu öğrenince biraz hayal kırıklığına uğradığımı itiraf etmeliyim çünkü ister inanın ister inanmayın, Carlos ve ben "merengue" dansını bayağı iyi kıvırmaya başlamıştık.

Ama birçok kişi çok heyecanlıydı çünkü Kasım ayından beri genel toplantı olmamıştı. Kasım'da okulumuza Müthiş Andrew adındaki hipnozcu gelmişti.

Gösterisinin büyük finalinde, Müthiş Andrew sekizinci sınıftan bir dizi öğrenciyi hipnotize etti ve kollarının birbirine tutkalla yapışık olduğunu düşünmelerini sağladı.

Sonra onlara kendilerini sihirli bir sözcükle ayıracağını söyledi. Müthiş Andrew bu sözcüğü söyler söylemez, oğlanlar gerçekten de ayrıldılar.

HIYAR!

Okuldan sonra bazı çocuklar hipnozcunun gerçek olup olmadığını ya da sekizinci sınıfların da gösteriye dahil olarak numara yapıp yapmadığını tartışmaya başladılar.

Müthiş Andrew'un sahtekâr olduğunu düşünen iki çocuk kol kola girdiler. Sonra Martin Ford onları hipnotize ederek birbirlerini tutkalla bağlı olduklarına ikna etmeye çalıştı.

İster inanın ister inanmayın, İŞE YARADI! İki çocuk kollarını birbirlerinden ayıramadılar ve büyük bir paniğe kapıldılar. Martin sihirli sözcüğü söylemeyi denedi ama onları ayırmayı başaramadı.

Çocuklar okula döndüler. Öğretmenlerden biri Müthiş Andrew'u işyerinden aramak ve çocukları ayırmak için sihirli sözcüğü söylemesini istemek zorunda kaldı.

Okulumuza gelip toplantı ve gösteriler yapan insanların nasıl seçildiği konusunda hiçbir fikrim yok. Geçen yıl bir de Güçlü Steve diye birini getirmişlerdi. Adam uyuşturucudan nasıl uzak durmamız gerektiği konusunda bir konuşma yaptı; sonra da büyük finalde bir telefon defterini elleriyle ortadan ikiye ayırdı.

CIRTTTTTTT

Telefon defterini yırtmakla uyuşturucudan uzak durmak arasında nasıl bir ilişki olduğunu bana sormayın. Ama okuldaki çocuklar bu adama deli oldular. Öyle ki, Güçlü Steve'in ziyaretinden sonra, kütüphane görevlisi raflardaki başvuru kitaplarının yarısının yerine yenilerini koymak zorunda kaldı.

Ben, Krisstina adındaki şarkıyı tekrar GETİRMEYECEKLERİNİ umuyorum. Sanırım okul Krisstina'yı, şarkı sözlerini çok olumlu ve iyimser buldukları için getirmek istiyor.

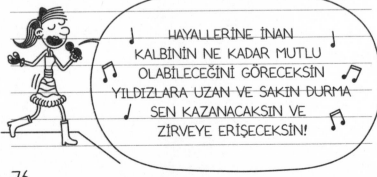

HAYALLERİNE İNAN KALBİNİN NE KADAR MUTLU OLABİLECEĞİNİ GÖRECEKSİN YILDIZLARA UZAN VE SAKIN DURMA SEN KAZANACAKSIN VE ZİRVEYE ERİŞECEKSİN!

Krisstina kendine "uluslararası pop yıldızı" diyor ama bunu nasıl söylüyor bilmiyorum. Bildiğim kadarıyla kendisi ÜLKE dışına hiç çıkmamış.

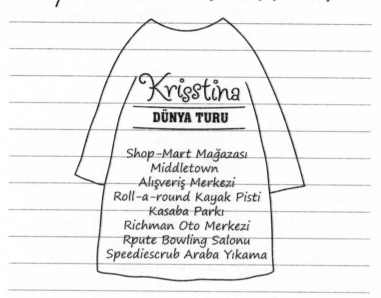

Ben en çok bir polisin okuluma geldiği ve bize "nark" (narkotiğin kısaltılması imiş) ajanı olmaktan söz ettiği toplantıyı sevdim. Görevi, bir lise öğrencisi gibi görünmek ve olmadık davranışlarda bulunan öğrencileri ihbar etmekmiş.

Bunun MÜTHİŞ bir iş olduğunu düşündüm.
Eğer ev ödevi yapmadan, sınavlara girmeden
okula gideceksem, bütün gıcıkları ve serserileri
hapse gönderebileceksem, bir de bunun üzerine
para alacaksam, bu iş tam bana göre!

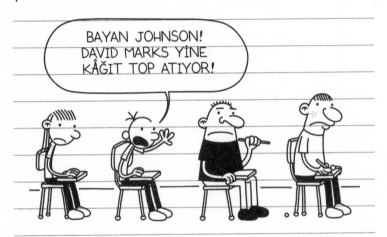

Polis memuru okulumuza geldikten sonra,
arkadaşım Rowley ve ben kendi dedektiflik
büromuzu kurmaya karar verdik.

Ne yazık ki, bizim mahallede özel dedektiflere pek talep yoktu. Kimse bizi tutmak istemedi. Ama biz yine de insanları gözetlemeye karar verdik.

Gerçekten çok eğlenceliydi. Özel dedektif olmanın en güzel tarafı, başka insanların hayatına burnunuzu sokabiliyorsunuz. Bu, işinizin bir parçası.

Özellikle bizim birkaç ev ötemizde oturan Bay
Millis'in hayatı üzerinde yoğunlaştık. Adamın
şüpheli bir şey yaptığı filan yoktu. Yalnızca
onun kablolu yayınında bütün sinema kanallarının
olduğunu biliyorduk.

Ancak Scotty Douglas'ı araştırmaya başladıktan
sonra, dedektiflik büromuz dağıldı. Ona yaz
için bir bilgisayar oyunu ödünç vermiştim;
kaybettiğini söyledi ama yalan söylediğini
biliyordum. Bu yüzden Rowley'i bu meseleyi
halletmesi için Scotty'nin evine gönderdim.

Rowley'e nasıl gerçekten sert davranacağını
ve parmaklarını nasıl çatırdatacağını öğrettim.
Böylece Scotty hiç şakamızın olmadığına dair
mesajı almış olacaktı.

Ancak Rowley hemen geri dönmeyince, neler olduğunu merak etmeye başladım. Bizzat araştırma yapmak için ben de Rowley'nin evine gittim ve Rowley'i, Scotty ile birlikte benim bilgisayar oyunumu oynarken suçüstü yakaladım.

Rowley'i hemen oracıkta kovmak zorunda kaldım. Bundan sonra bir dedektiflik ajansı kuracak olursam, ilk işim daha korkutucu bir eleman bulmak olacak.

Her neyse, söylediğim gibi, herkes bugünkü konuğun kim olduğunu duyunca çok heyecanlandı.

Ama sonra ortada konuk filan OLMADIĞI anlaşıldı. Spor salonunda yerlerimizi aldığımızda, Müdür Yardımcısı Roy sahneye çıktı ve bizi toplamasının nedenini açıkladı. Öğrenci meclisinin yenilenmesi için özel bir seçim yapılacakmış.

Öğrenci meclisi seçimlerini geçen sonbaharda yapmıştık. Ancak sınıf temsilcileri, teneffüslerde oyuna daldıkları için toplantıları kaçırıyorlardı. Bu yüzden yönetimdekilerin canına tak etti galiba.

Müdür Yardımcısı Roy, temsilci seçilmek için iki şartın olduğunu söyledi. Birincisi, bütün öğrenci meclisi toplantılarına katılmaya gönüllü olmak. İkincisi, üç ya da daha fazla disiplin cezası almamış olmak.

Üçüncü kuralın hedefinin BEN olduğumu düşündüm çünkü geçenlerde üçüncü disiplin cezamı aldım.

Ortaokulun ilk yılında, bir sekizinci sınıf öğrencisi bana ikinci katta gizli bir asansör olduğunu, beş papel karşılığında bana bu asansör için özel bir geçiş kartı verebileceğini söyledi.

Bu BANA harika bir anlaşma gibi geldi. Çok resmi görünen geçiş kartını almak için ona beş papel verdim.

ASANSÖR GEÇİŞ KARTI

Bu kartın sahibi,
ortaokul asansörünü
sınırsız sayıda kullanabilir.

Ama sonra bunun tamamen bir üçkâğıtçılık olduğu, böyle gizli bir asansör filan bulunmadığı ortaya çıktı.

O zamandan beri bu kartı elimde tutuyordum. Ama birkaç hafta önce onu okula yeni gelen bir çocuğa sattım.

Ne yazık ki ben dikkatli davranmamışım. Müdür Yardımcısı Roy'a enselendim ve parayı iade etmek zorunda kaldım.

Üstelik Müdür Yardımcısı Roy bana disiplin cezası da verdi! Ama bu haksızlık; çünkü kartı çocuğa yarı fiyatına satarak büyük iyilik etmiştim aslında.

Toplantıdan sonra bir şey fark ettim: Rowley hiç disiplin cezası almadı; bu yüzden MÜKEMMEL bir öğrenci meclisi temsilcisi adayı olabilir. Ona girişimde bulunması gerektiğini söyledim. Ama seçilirse ne yapacağını bilemeyeceğini söyledi.

Ben de o anda devreye girdim. Ona seçilirse, bütün zor kararları benim vereceğimi, onun sadece toplantılara katılmasının ve benim ona söylediklerimi yapmasının yeterli olacağını anlattım. Bence bu DAHİCE bir fikir. Çünkü böylece hem güç benim elimde olacak hem de teneffüsleri kaçırmak zorunda kalmayacağım.

Onun kampanya yöneticisi olmaya da gönüllüydüm; böylece seçilmek için parmağını bile kıpırdatmak zorunda kalmayacaktı. Böylece ön koridordaki panoya gittik ve Rowley'in adını adaylar listesine yazdık.

Rowley'e Başkan ya da Başkan Yardımcılığı gibi havalı görevler için aday olması gerektiğini söyledim. Ama o, "Sosyal Başkan" olmak istiyordu. Sosyal Başkan'ın ne yaptığı konusunda hiçbir fikrim yok. Ama Rowley önemli kararlar için oy kullanma hakkına sahip olduğu sürece, bana göre hava hoş.

Çarşamba

Dün diğer adaylardan bazıları koridorlara afişler asıyor, oy toplamak için şeker, rozet filan dağıtıyorlardı. Yani biz ŞİMDİDEN geride kalmıştık.

Rowley'in seçileceğinden emin olmak için büyük bir şey hayal edip yaratmam gerektiğini biliyordum. Ben de şunu buldum:

Adaylar spor salonunda konuşmalarını yaparlarken, tribünler öğrencilerle dolu olacak. Televizyonda izlediğim spor karşılaşmalarında, stadyumdaki insanlar göğüslerine harfler asarak sözcükler oluşturup mesaj vermeye çalışıyorlar.

Dün gece Gary Amca'nın garajdaki tişörtlerinden bir yığın aldım ve her birinin üzerine bir harf yazdım. Harfler bir araya gelince "SOSYAL BAŞKANLIK İÇİN ROWLEY JEFFERSON'A OY VER" cümlesini oluşturuyordu. Bütün gece bununla uğraştım, neredeyse yirmi kalem bitirdim ama bunun toplantıda büyük sükse yapacağını biliyordum.

Bugün okula erken gittim ve tişörtlerden giymeye gönüllü olan her çocuğa birer sakız verdim.

Ama spor salonuna gittiğimizde, çocukları doğru sıraya dizmek, deveye hendek atlatmaktan zor oldu.

Yalnızca Başkanlık için aday olanlar konuşma yapacaklardı. Bunu duyunca rahatladım çünkü Rowley, ben ona Sosyal Başkanlık için konuşmasının provasını yaptırırken heyecandan saçmaladı durdu.

SELAMLAR, ÖĞRENCİKLER....
BENİM ADIM ROWLEY JEFFERSON
VE BEN... ŞEY..."

Konuşma yapacak ilk aday, Sydney Green adında bir kızdı. Sürekli A alır ve bir gün bile okula devamsızlık yapmazdı. Sydney, Başkan seçilirse, müzik odası için daha iyi aletler alacağını, kütüphanedeki kitapların daha koruyucu kapakları olması konusunda da bir proje geliştireceğini söyledi.

Sonra sıra Bryan Buttsy'ye geldi. Müdür Yardımcısı Roy, Bryan'ı kürsüye çağırır çağırmaz, spor salonundaki herkes iğrenç sesler çıkarmaya başladı.

Eminim Bryan konuşması sırasında bir sürü ilgi çekici şey söylemiştir ama o şamatanın arasında tek bir sözcüğü bile duymak imkânsızdı.

Umarım Bryan büyüyünce Devlet Başkanlığı'na filan adaylığını koymaz çünkü eğer bunu yaparsa, seçim mitingleri çok SAÇMA SAPAN geçer.

Son aday, Eugene Ellis adında bir çocuktu. Eugene başkanlığa aday olup da afiş asmayan ya da lolipop filan dağıtmayan tek kişi. Bu yüzden kimse onu ciddiye almadı.

Eugene'nin kampanya konuşması yalnızca otuz saniye sürdü. Eğer başkan seçilirse, okulun tuvaletindeki ucuz tuvalet kâğıtlarının yerine pahalı, kaliteli tuvalet kâğıtları konmasını sağlayacağını söyledi.

Eugene konuşmasını bitirdiğinde, herkes çılgına dönmüştü. Çocuklar, HEP tuvalet kâğıdı meselesinden şikâyet ediyorlar çünkü okulun kullandığı tuvalet kâğıdı, zımpara kâğıdı gibi.

Eugene'in gördüğü ilgiye bakılacak olursa,
Sydney ve Bryan'ın hiç şansı yok bence.

Perşembe

Tam tahmin ettiğim gibi, Eugene açık ara
farkla öğrenci meclisi başkanı seçildi. Rowley de
kazandı çünkü Sosyal Başkanlık için adaylığını
koyan tek kişi oydu. Keşke bunu bilseydim;
tişörtlerle o kadar uğraşmaktan kurtulurdum.

Öğrenci meclisi bugün ilk toplantısını
yaptı. Meclisle çalışan öğretmen, Bayan
Birch, Eugene'ye okulun tuvaletlere kaliteli
tuvalet kâğıdı koyacak parasının olmadığını, bu
yüzden bunu unutması gerektiğini söyledi.

Bu haber okulda hızla yayıldı ve herkes çok öfkelendi. Herkesin Eugene'ye oy vermesinin tek nedeni, onun kampanyada verdiği sözdü. Üstelik her yıl hepimiz, okula yardım toplamak için çalışıyoruz. Kazandığımız paranın bir bölümünü de kaliteli tuvalet kâğıdı almak için harcayabilirler herhalde.

Birkaç hafta önce düzenlenen SON yardım kampanyasından sonra, okulun zengin olduğunu düşünüyordum. Gofret satmıştık. Bu fikir kimin aklına geldiyse, hakkını vermek lazım. Okul, her öğrenciyi eve elli tane çikolatalı gofret ile gönderdi. Dışarı çıkıp bunları komşularımıza satmamız gerekiyordu.

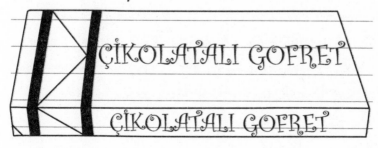

ÇİKOLATALI GOFRET

ÇİKOLATALI GOFRET

Ama daha eve varmadan üç ya da dört gofreti mideye indirmeyen tek bir çocuk bile olmadı. Bense, annem beni yakalayıp buna bir son verene kadar tam on beş gofret yemiştim.

Bu yüzden, benim ailem gibi birçok aile, çocuklarının yediği gofretlerin parasını okula ödemek zorunda kaldı. Belki de bu yardım kampanyası sırasında hiç kimse tek bir gofret bile satmamıştır.

Cumartesi
Paradan söz etmişken, Gary Amca bu hafta bütün harçlığını bitirmiş. Bana kendisine BENİM harçlığımdan borç verip veremeyeceğimi sordu. Babam bunu öğrenince, sinirden deliye döndü.

94

Gary Amca'nın bütün parasını piyango biletlerine harcadığı ortaya çıktı. Babam da ona, kendisini yıldırım çarpma olasılığının piyangodan para kazanma olasılığından daha büyük olduğunu, bu yaptığının parasını çarçur etmekten başka bir şey olmadığını söyledi.

Bence babam sözcüklerini daha dikkatli seçmeliydi çünkü Manny bunu duyduğundan beri yağmurda dışarı adım atmak istemiyor.

Piyango meselesi, babam için tam bir kanayan yara. Birkaç yıl önce babam, Gary Amca'ya Noel armağanı olarak çok güzel bir kışlık ceket almıştı. Gary Amca da babama piyango bileti armağan etti. Babam, kendisi Gary Amca için onca para harcamışken Gary Amca'nın ona bu kadar ucuz bir armağan vermesine biraz bozulmuş gibiydi.

Babam kartın üzerindeki küçük kareleri bozuk parayla kazıdı ve üç kiraz buldu. Bu da yüz bin dolar kazandığı anlamına geliyordu.

Ama sonra bunun bir şaka, biletin de sahte olduğu ortaya çıktı.

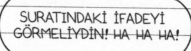

Babamın yanında hâlâ o Noel'den söz edemiyoruz. Çünkü ne zaman bunu konuşsak günün geri kalanını suratı bir karış asık halde, keyifsiz geçiriyor!

Babamın tek istediği, Gary Amca'nın bir iş bulup bizim evden taşınması. Ben de Gary Amca'nın bir iş bulmasını yürekten dilemeye başladım çünkü son zamanlarda bütün zamanını benim odamda bilgisayarda oyun oynayarak geçirmeye başladı.

Canın ne isterse o olabileceğin —polis, inşaat işçisi ya da rock yıldızı— olabileceğin sanal dünya oyununa bağımlı hale geldi.

Ama Gary Amca oyunda işi olmayan ve her gün piyango biletleri alan bir adam.

ŞUBAT

<u>Perşembe</u>
Bu hafta okulda çok büyük gelişmeler oldu.

Her şey pazartesi günü son öğrenci meclisi toplantısında başladı. Toplantılar öğretmenler odasında yapılıyor. Sayman Javan Hill, tuvalete gittiğinde, elinde bir rulo Minder Yumuşaklığı-Ultra tuvalet kâğıdıyla dönmüş.

Bunun anlamı şu: Biz öğrenciler ucuz tuvalet kâğıdına mahkûm edilirken, öğretmenler kendilerine kaliteli tuvalet kâğıdı alıyorlar!

Eugene Ellis, Bayan Birch ile yüzleştiğinde, öğretmenlerin bu işe çok bozulduğunun farkındaymış.

Bayan Birch, öğretmenler Minder-Yumuşaklığı-Ultra tuvalet kâğıdı kullanıyor olsalar da, bütçede bütün öğrenci tuvaletlerine pahalı tuvalet kâğıdı koyacak kadar para olmadığını ama bir uzlaşma yolu bulacağını söylemiş.

Öğrencilerin kendi tuvalet kâğıtlarını EVLERİNDEN getirmelerine izin verilebilirmiş. Okulun hoparlörlerinden duyuru yapıldığında, bu Eugene Ellis ve öğrenci meclisi için büyük bir zafer oldu.

Salı günü. Öğrencilerin evden tuvalet kâğıdı getirmelerine izin verilen ilk gündü. Sanırım bazıları işi abartmışlardı.

Kimileri o kadar çok tuvalet kâğıdı getirmişti ki, dolaplarda bunları koyacak yer kalmadı. Onlar da malzemeleri yanlarında taşımak zorunda kaldılar.

Her şey yolunda gidecekti aslında ama öğle yemeğinde biri, başka birine bir rulo tuvalet kâğıdı fırlattı. On beş saniye içinde de ortalık tımarhaneye döndü.

O gün öğleden sonra müdür hoparlörden yeni bir duyuru yaptı ve bundan sonra okula günde yalnızca beş parça tuvalet kâğıdı getirebileceğimizi söyledi. Bence bu çok saçma bir kural çünkü günde beş parça ile HİÇ KİMSENİN idare edebileceğini sanmıyorum.

Dün, yanında getirmesi gerekenden fazla tuvalet kâğıdı getiren birkaç çocuk yakalandı. Bu yüzden artık öğretmenler sabahları kapıdan girerken çantalarımızı arıyorlar.

Perşembe

Geçen hafta müdür beş parça kuralını koyduğunda, ben dolabıma yaklaşık yirmi rulo tuvalet kâğıdı stoklamıştım bile.

Öğretmenler şimdi öğrencilerin dolaplarında rasgele arama yapıyorlar. Er ya da geç benim stoğumu da ortaya çıkaracaklarını biliyordum.

Stoğumun yıl sonuna kadar yeteceğinden emin olmak istiyordum; bu yüzden onu korumanın bir yolunu bulmalıydım.

Bunun TEK yolunun tuvalette kendime özel bir kabinimin olması ve tuvalet kâğıtlarımı oraya saklamak olduğuna karar verdim.

Böylece pazartesi günü çok temiz bir kabin seçtim ve kapıyı kilitledim. Kapının altından emekleyerek çıktım.

Sonra, içerisi dolu görünsün diye, evden getirdiğim eski spor ayakkabıları içeri soktum.

Bu hafta ne zaman tuvalete gitmem gerekse, etrafı kollayıp kimsenin olmamasına dikkat ettim. Sonra kabinimin kapısının altından emekleyerek girdim. Sanki orada küçük bir apartman dairem varmış gibiydi. Keşke bu fikir uzun süre önce aklıma gelseydi.

Birkaç gün boyunca sistemim kusursuz işledi. Hiç kimse benim özel kabinimi kullanmayı DENEMEDİ bile.

Ama sonra yedek ayakkabılardan birini yerden almayı unuttum ve sanırım bu, dışarıdan bakıldığında şüphe uyandırıcı göründü.

Çok geçmeden insanlar benim kaliteli tuvalet kâğıdı istiflediğimi anladılar ve kısa süre içinde her şey altüst oldu.

Cuma

Bence öğrencilerin tuvalet kâğıdı deneyiminden aldığı ders şu oldu: Eğer bir şey istiyorsak, kendi başımızın çaresine bakmak zorundayız.

Bu yüzden geçen hafta öğrenci meclisi, sınıf için yardım toplamak konusunda beyin fırtınası yaptı ve fikirler ortaya attı. Başkan Yardımcısı, Hillary Pine, araba yıkayabileceğimizi söyledi. Olivia Dabis ise büyük bir bahçe pazarı kurmamızı önerdi.

Ben patlamış mısır satmamız gerektiğini düşünüyordum ama ya Rowley telsizini açmamıştı ya da herkes beni duymazdan geliyordu.

Eugene Ellis, spor salonunda bir profesyonel güreş karşılaşması önerdi. Javan Hill, motosiklet gösterisi fikrini ortaya attı. Ama hangi fikri daha çok sevdiklerine karar veremediler ve motosiklet-güreş karışımı bir etkinlik konusunda anlaştılar.

Sanırım Eugene böyle bir şeyi düzenlemek için çok çalışmak gerekeceğini anladı ve bu işi Başkan Yardımcısı'na devretti. Hillary bir Yardım Toplama Komitesi oluşturdu ve öğrenci meclisindeki arkadaşlarının buna katılmasını sağladı.

Pazartesi günü, Hillary öğrenci meclisine rapor verdi ve etkinlik için her şeyin planlandığını ama Yardım Toplama Komitesi'nin orijinal fikir üzerinde birkaç "küçük değişiklik" yaptığını söyledi.

Nasıl olduysa, motosiklet /güreş etkinliği, SEVGİLİLER GÜNÜ dansına dönüşmüş. Eugene ve diğerleri bunu tekrar değiştirmek istediler ama Bayan Birch, Yardım Toplama Komitesi'nin kararına saygı duymaları gerektiğini söyledi. Ben işin aslının başka olduğundan, Bayan Birch'in spor salonuna motorlu araçların girmesi fikrine bayılmadığından eminim.

Sevgililer Günü dansı haberi yayıldığından beri, okulda herkes bunu konuşuyor. Kızlar, çok heyecanlanmış görünüyorlar ve sanırım bunu bir tür ortaokul balosu gibi görüyorlar.

Dans Komitesi kuruldu bile. Rowley de Sosyal Başkan olduğu için komiteye davet edildi. Komitede erkek temsilci bulunmasına memnun oldum; çünkü iş kızlara kalsaydı, o gecenin eğlencesi olarak Krisstina'yı davet ederlerdi.

Oğlanların çoğunun dansla ilgilendiği yok. Bir grup çocuğun, okulun spor salonundaki bir dansa gitmek için asla üç papel vermeyeceklerini söylediklerini duydum. Ama geçen hafta sınıfta ilk Şeker Kalpler dağıtılınca, her şey değişti.

Şeker Kalpler, Sevgililer Günü dansının davetiyeleri. Dans Komitesi geçen gün öğle yemeğinden sonra bunları satmaya başladı. Yirmi beş sent verdiğinizde, istediğiniz birine Şeker Kalp gönderebiliyorsunuz. Bryce Anderson'a en az beş farklı kızdan Şeker Kalp gelmişti.

Sevgili *Bryce*,

Sevgililer Günü dansına benimle birlikte katılsan ne "tatlı" olur!

İmza:

Jessica

Şeker Kalpler'in ilk dalgası dağıtıldıktan sonra hiç Şeker Kalp alamayan oğlanlar alanları kıskandılar. Şimdi HERKES dansa gitmek istiyor çünkü dışlanmak istemiyor. Bu yüzden dün öğle yemeğinde Şeker Kalpler'e birden büyük ilgi oldu.

Daha önce dediğim gibi, bu yıl bizim sınıfta oğlanların sayısı kızlardan çok daha fazla. Bu yüzden sanırım bir sürü oğlan, dansa birlikte gideceği birini bulamamaktan korkuyor. Bu yüzden çoğu, etrafta bir kız varken, gerçekten çok farklı davranıyor.

Öğle yemeğinde, oğlanlar kaşıklarla patates püresi alıyorlar ve bunları yukarı fırlatıp tavana yapıştırmaya çalışıyorlar.

Patateslerin böyle yapışması için içine NE koyduklarını sormayın bana!

Bazen oturacak bir yer bulmadan önce başımı kaldırıp yukarı bakmayı unutuyorum.

Kızlar, bu patates püresi meselesinden nefret ediyorlar. Bu yüzden kantinin öbür ucunda oturuyorlar. Ama artık oğlanlar, böyle serseri gibi davranmaları durumunda kızların hiçbirinden Şeker Kalp alamayacaklarını biliyorlar.

Birçok oğlan için kızların yanında olgun davranmanın çok zor olduğunu biliyorum. Bu yüzden bazıları etrafta kızlar yokken her türlü yaramazlığı yapıyorlar.

Beden Eğitimi dersinde, basketbol çalışmasının tam ortasındaydık. Kızlar spor salonunun bir tarafında, oğlanlar diğer tarafında oynuyordu. Geçen gün, Anthony Renfrew adındaki çocuk, Daniel Revis serbest atış yaparken onun şortunu indirmenin çok komik olacağını düşündü.

Daniel dışında herkes kahkahalarla güldü ama sonra Daniel, bir atış yapmaya hazırlanan Anthony'den intikamını aldı. Biraz sonra herkes birbirinin şortunu aşağı indiriyordu. O zamandan beri her şey ÇOK KÖTÜ.

Artık herkes birinin şortunu indireceği paranoyasını yaşadığından, basketbol antrenmanı sırasında kimse ayağa kalkmıyor.

Ben de kendimi iyice emniyete almak için, eşofmanımın altına iki şort giymeye başladım.

İşler öyle kötü bir hal almaya başladı ki, bugün Müdür Yardımcısı Roy spor salonuna geldi ve oğlanlara nutuk çekti. Bunda gülünecek bir şey olmadığını, bundan sonra başka bir öğrencinin şortunu indirmeye kalkan kişinin okuldan uzaklaştırılacağını söyledi.

Ama Müdür Yardımcısı Roy'un durduğu yer konusunda daha dikkatli olması gerekirdi. Çünkü çocuklardan biri bankların altına girdi ve onu hazırlıksız yakaladı.

Bunu her kim yaptıysa, Müdür Yardımcısı Roy'un kendisini yakalamasına fırsat vermeden kaçtı. Kimse onun kim olduğundan emin değil ama kendisine Deli Şort adını taktılar.

Salı

Şeker Kalpler ortaya çıkalı yaklaşık bir hafta oldu ve ben de henüz hiç Şeker Kalp almadığım için endişelenmeye başladım. Hayatım boyunca tavana patates püresi fırlatmadım, kimsenin şortunu da indirmedim. Bu yüzden günümüzde bir erkeğin bir kızı etkilemek için ne yapması gerektiğini merak ediyorum.

Sınıftaki oğlanların her birine bir Şeker Kalp gelmiş gibi görünüyor. Travis Hickey'ye bile bir tane geldi. Oysa kendisi, üç beş kuruş karşılığında çöp tenekesinden çıkmış pizza artıklarını bile yer.

Önceki gece, Gary Amca benim odamda bilgisayarda oyun oynuyordu. Ona Sevgililer Günü Dansı'ndan ve Şeker Kalpler'den söz ettim. İster inanın ister inanmayın, çok güzel öğütler verdi bana.

Gary Amca, bir kızın ilgisini çekmenin en iyi yolunun kendini "ulaşılmaz" göstermek olduğunu söyledi. Bir sürü Şeker Kalp satın alıp KENDİME göndermeliymişim. Böylece kızlar benim kaçırılmaması gereken popüler biri olduğumu düşünürlermiş.

Keşke Gary Amca ile konuşmayı çok daha önce
akıl etseymişim. Kendisi dört kere evlendi; bu
yüzden ilişkiler konusunda UZMAN.

Dün iki dolarlık Şeker Kalp aldım; bugün sınıfta
bunlar bana teslim edildi.

GREG HEFFLEY İÇİN
BİR TANE DAHA!

AYYH!

Umarım bu işe yarar çünkü iki dolar benim öğle
yemeği paramdı.

Cuma

Çarşamba gününe kadar beş dolarım uçup gitmişti. Kendim için Şeker Kalpler almaya devam edersem, açlıktan öleceğimi fark ettim. Bu yüzden bir KIZ için Şeker Kalp almaya ve bu durumda işlerin nasıl gideceğini görmeye karar verdim.

Dün öğle yemeğinde bir Şeker Kalp alıp Adrianne Simpson'a gönderdim. Kendisi İngilizce dersinde benim birkaç sıra ötemde oturuyor. Ama bütün paramı tek bir kişi için riske atmak istemediğimden, kendimi garantiye aldım.

Sevgili Adrianne,

Sevgililer Günü Dansı'na
benimle birlikte katılsan
ne "tatlı" olur!

İmza:
Greg Heffley

Not: Eğer cevabın
hayır ise, bunu

sol tarafında iki sıra önünde oturan Julia Barros'a aktarır mısın?

Bu sabah sınıfa girdiğimde, Adrianne ve Julia bana kötü kötü bakıyorlardı. Bu yüzden ikisinin cevabının da hayır olduğunu varsayıyorum.

Bu arada bir kızı dansa davet etmenin TEK yolunun Şeker Kalp olmadığını fark ettim. Sınıfta, benim tarih dersinde oturduğum sırada oturan Leighann Marlow adında bir kız var. Ben de masamın üzerine onun için bir not yazdım. Bu yüzden para harcamam da gerekmedi.

Ne yazık ki, okuldan sonra cezaya kalanların bu sınıfta tutulduğunu unutmuşum. Gerizekâlının biri, Leighann'in notumu okumasına fırsat bırakmadan bir cevap yazmış.

Selam Leighann
Eğer dansa birlikte gidebileceğin birini arıyorsan, buraya yazarak bana bildir yeter.
                    Greg Heffley

Selam Greg
Çok üzgünüm ama seninle dansa gitmek istemiyorum.
                    Leighann

Sevgili Greg
Evet, seninle dansa giderim.
Not: Benimle evlenir misin?

KISS KISS

KIH KIH
        KIH

119

Çok gerginim çünkü görünüşe göre bu noktadan sonra aralarından seçim yapabileceğim pek fazla kız kalmadı.

Henüz kimseye sözü olan kızlardan biri Erika Hernandez. Kendisi, erkek arkadaşı olan Jamar Law'dan yeni ayrıldı. Jamar, okulda kafasını iskemleye sıkıştırmakla ünlü. Temizlik görevlisi, iskemleyi testereyle keserek onu kurtarmak zorunda kalmıştı. Hepsi okul yıllığında var.

Abuk Subuk Bir Durum: Jamar Law, Bayan Moran'ın resim dersinde kafasını iskemleye sıkıştırınca, Bay Lewis imdadına yetişti.

Erika gerçekten çok güzel ve hoş bir kız. Bu yüzden Jamar gibi bir denyo ile ne diye çıktığını sormayın bana.

Erika benim dans listemin en başında olabilirdi.
Ama onunla aramda her şey yolunda giderse,
sürekli eski erkek arkadaşını düşüneceğimden,
bunu atlatamayacağımdan endişelendim.

Erika Hernandez'in durumu, diğer kızların
hayatında da Jamar Law gibi tipler olup
olmadığını merak etmeme yol açtı. Okulda kimin
kiminle çıktığının kaydını tutmak zor ve dansa
birlikte gideceğin birini ararken bu önemli bir
bilgi. Bu yüzden sınıfımdaki herkesin birbiriyle
ilişkisini gösteren bir şema çizdim.

Daha çok işi var ama tamamlanmamış hali şu:

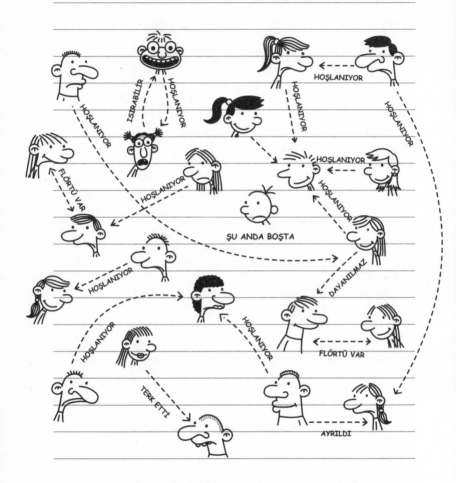

Şemada beni endişelendiren çocuk Evan
Whitehead. Onun bizim sınıftaki bir sürü kızı
öptüğünü söyleyip durduğunu duydum.

Ama geçen hafta Evan, suçiçeğine yakalandığı için okuldan eve gönderildi. Hâlâ bu hastalığa yakalanılabildiğini bilmiyordum. Kim bilir kaç kıza mikrop bulaştırmıştır!

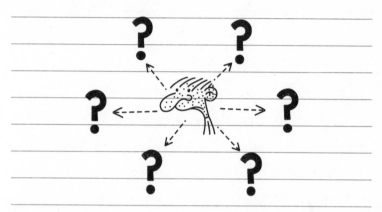

Evan'ın asla öpmediğinden kesinlikle emin olduğum kızlardan biri, Julie Webber. Çünkü Julie beşinci sınıftan beri Ed Norwell ile çıkıyor. Ama bugünlerde ilişkilerinin biraz sallantıda olduğunu duydum. Bu yüzden işleri hızlandırmak için elimden geleni yapmayı düşünüyorum.

<u>Salı</u>

Gary Amca bana eğer bir kızın benimle dansa gelmesini istiyorsam, onunla yüz yüze konuşmam gerektiğini söyledi. Ben bundan kaçınmaya çalışıyordum ama belki de haklıdır.

Sınıfta hep bir şekilde ilgi duyduğum Peyton Ellis adında bir kız var. Dün onu musluktan su içerken gördüğümde, durdum ve sabırla işini bitirmesini bekledim. Ama Peyton beni göz ucuyla görmüş ve kendisini dansa davet edeceğimi anlamış olmalı ki, ben orada salak gibi dikilirken su içmeye devam etti.

Sonunda zil çaldı ve ikimiz de sınıfa girmek zorunda kaldık.

Peytoni doğru dürüst tanımıyorum, bu yüzden belki de ona teklifte bulunmaya çalışmak kötü bir fikirdi. Öyle ya da böyle bağlantımın olduğu kızlara teklif etmemin daha iyi olacağını anladım. Aklıma gelen ilk kişi, Fen Bilgisi dersindeki laboratuvar eşim Bethany Breen idi.

Ama Bethany üzerinde pek iyi bir izlenim bıraktığımı sanmıyorum. Anatomi dersindeydik ve son birkaç gündür kurbağaları parçalıyorduk. Ben böyle şeylerden çok iğrenirim; bu yüzden parçalama işini Bethany'ye bıraktım ve ben sınıfın öbür ucunda durup kusmamaya çalıştım.

Bugün, bu çağda neden içlerinde ne olduğunu görmek için kurbağaları açıyorlar, anlamış değilim gerçekten!

Biri bana kurbağanın içinde bir kalp ve bağırsak olduğunu söylese, ona inanırım gider.

Laboratuvarda Bethany ile eş olduğum için çok mutluydum. Hatırlıyorum da, ilkokuldayken ne zaman bir öğretmen bir kızla bir oğlanı eşleştirse, diğer çocuklar ÇILDIRIRDI:

Laboratuvarda Bethany ile eş olduğumda, sınıfın geri kalanından bir tepki bekliyordum. Ama sanırım herkes böyle şeylerden bıkmıştı artık.

Kurbağa parçalama konusundaki becerilerimle Bethany'yi etkileyemesem de, yine de onun karşısında bir şansım olabileceğini düşünüyordum. Övünmek filan istemiyorum ama ben gerçekten müthiş bir laboratuvar eşiyim.

Dün gün sonunda, Bethany'nin yanına gittim. Dolaptan montunu alıyordu.

Her gün kırk beş dakikayı laboratuvar eşi olarak geçirsek de, onunla konuşurken biraz heyecanlanıp gerildiğimi itiraf etmeliyim. Ama daha tek kelime edemeden, aklıma kurbağalar geldi. Bethany ile ilişkimizin yürüyeceğini sanmıyorum.

Dün gece, Gary Amca'ya okulda olanları anlatıyordum. Sorunumun bunu tek başıma yapmaya çalışmam olduğunu, kızlara cazip görünmek için bir "yancı"ya, yani çirkin kızları oyalayıp kendini feda edecek birine ihtiyacım olduğunu söyledi.

Sanırım Rowley MÜKEMMEL bir "yancı" olabilir. Çünkü onun yanında kendim gibi davrandığımda bile iyi görünüyorum.

Bugün Rowley'den benim "yancım" olmasını istedim, durumu anlattım ama pek anlamadı. Ben de bir anlamda dans için kampanya yöneticim olacağını söyledim.

Rowley o zaman ikimizin de birbirimizin "yancısı" olabileceğimizi, dansta eş bulmak konusunda birbirimize yardımcı olabileceğimizi söyledi.
Ben de bunu sırayla yapmamız gerektiğini açıkladım. İçimden bir ses önce benim durumumla ilgilenmemiz gerektiğini söylüyor çünkü Rowley'e dans eşi bulmak uzun vadeli bir proje olabilir.

Bu "yancı" meselesini öğle yemeğinde denedik. Ama bence daha katetmemiz gereken uzun bir yol var.

Perşembe

Bugün okuldan eve dönerken, Rowley, Dans Komitesi'nden Alyssa Grove adındaki bir kızın erkek arkadaşından yeni ayrıldığını ve dansa gitmek için kendine bir eş aradığını duyduğunu söyledi.

Gördünüz mü? İşte bu yüzden Rowley'i yancım ilan ettim. Alyssa bizim okulun en popüler kızlarından biri. Diğer açıkgözlerden biri onu kapmadan önce, hızlı hareket etmek zorundaydım.

Eve gider gitmez hemen Alyssa'nın numarasını çevirdim. Ama cevap vermedi. Telesekreter o kadar hızlı devreye girdi ki bir anda kendimi mesaj bırakırken buldum.

Mesajımı silmek ve baştan başlamak için telefonda bir düğmeye bastım. Ama ikinci mesajım da pek başarılı olmadı.

Yirmi mesaj filan kaydetmiş olmalıyım çünkü kusursuz olsun istiyordum. Ama Rowley de benimle birlikte odadaydı ve çok sessiz durmaya çalışıyordu. Ben de ne zaman ona baksam, dağılıyordum.

Biraz sonra Rowley ve ben gerçekten çok eğleniyor ve dalga geçiyorduk.

Rowley bizim evdeyken, ciddi bir mesaj bırakmamın imkânsız olduğunu anlamıştım. Bu yüzden son mesajı da silip telefonu kapattım. Yarına kadar bekleyip Alyssa ile yüz yüze konuşabileceğimi düşündüm.

Ama meğer benim bastığım düğme, Grove'ların telefonundaki mesajları silmiyormuş (bizim telefondakileri siliyor!). Bu yüzden bu gece akşam yemeğinden sonra kapı çalındı. Gelen, Alyssa'nın babasıydı.

Bay Grove, babama arkadaşımla benim onun telesekreterine münasebetsiz mesajlar bıraktığımızı, bundan sonra evlerini aramazsak çok memnun olacağını söyledi.

Yani sanırım Alyssa'yı da listemden silmem gerekecek.

Pazartesi

Gary Amca bana, eğer okuldaki kızlara doğru sinyaller göndermek istiyorsam, gardrobumu yenilemeyi düşünmemin iyi olabileceğini söyledi. Yeni bir gömlek ya da yeni ayakkabılar giymek onun özgüvenini artırırmış, benim için de bu işe yarayabilirmiş.

Mesele şu: Benim çok fazla yeni giysim YOK. Giydiklerimin %90'ı Rodrick'ten bana kalanlar. Annem abarttığımı düşünüyor ama kanıt istiyorsanız, iç çamaşırlarımdaki etiketlere bakabilirsiniz.

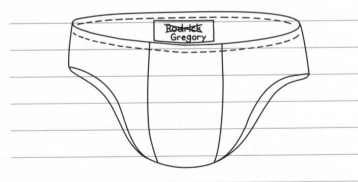

Ne giydiğim benim için önemli olmamıştır hiç. Ama şimdi Gary Amca yüzünden, gardrobumun benim şansımı azaltıp azaltmadığını düşünmeye başlamıştım.

Bu hafta sonu anneme alışverişe gidip bana yeni kot pantolon ve ayakkabılar alıp alamayacağımızı sordum. Böylece okulda çok fiyakalı görünebilirdim. Ama bunu söyler söylemez pişman oldum.

Annem bana ortaokula giden çocukların nasıl dış görünümlerine çok fazla önem verdikleri, ne giyeceğimize karar vermeye çalışarak geçirdiğimiz zamanın yarısını derslerimize ayırsak, ülkemizin dünyada matematik sıralamasında yirmi beşinci olmayacağı konusunda uzun bir nutuk çekti.

Annemin hemen dışarı koşup bana bir sürü yeni giysi almayacağını bilmem gerekirdi. Annem okul aile birliğinde ve okul üniformasının zorunlu olmasını sağlamaya çalıştı. Çünkü üniforma giyen çocukların derslerinde daha başarılı olduklarını söyleyen bir makale okumuş.

Neyse ki yeterince imza toplayamadı. Ama okulda üniforma zorunluluğu çalışmalarını annemin başlattığı haberi yayıldı. Ben de birkaç hafta boyunca, her gün eve sağ salim gidebilmek için yarım saat beklemek zorunda kaldım.

Annem beni giysi alışverişine götürmeyeceği için, ben de evi karıştırmaya ve giyebileceğim güzel bir şeyler var mı diye bakmaya karar verdim.

Önce Rodrick'in şifoniyerinin çekmecelerini karıştırdım ama giysiler konusunda zevklerimiz pek aynı değil bence.

Gary Amca, babamın dolabına bakmam gerektiğini söyledi. Çünkü bazen yetişkinlerin çok havalı görünebilecek "vintage" (o ne demekse!) kıyafetleri olabilirmiş. Hayatım boyunca babamı havalı bir şeyler giyerken görmedim. Ama yine de şansımı deneyebilirdim.

İyi ki Gary Amca bana bu tüyoyu vermiş. Çünkü ister inanın ister inanmayın, babamın dolabının arka tarafında TAM aradığım şeyi buldum.

SİYAH DERİ CEKETTİ bu. Babamın bunu giydiğini görmemiştim hiç. Ben daha doğmadan önce satın almış olmalıydı.

Babamın bu kadar havalı bir şeye sahip olduğu konusunda hiçbir fikrim yoku. Birden ona çok farklı bakmaya başlamıştım.

Ceketi giyip aşağı indim. Babam eski deri ceketini görünce çok şaşırdı. Bunu annemle çıkmaya başladığı günlerde aldığını söyledi.

Babama ceketi ödünç alıp alamayacağımı sordum. Kendisinin artık ihtiyacının olmadığını, alabileceğimi söyledi.

Ne yazık ki annem bu fikre sıcak bakmadı. Ceketin, bir ortaokul öğrencisinin giyemeyeceği kadar pahalı olduğunu, onu kaybedebileceğimi ya da bir yerine zarar verebileceğimi söyledi.

Ben de bunun haksızlık olduğunu, çünkü ceketin dolapta toz içinde öylece durduğunu söyleyerek karşı çıktım. Yani başına bir şey gelse de bir önemi yoktu aslında. Ama annem ceketin "yanlış mesaj" verdiğini, üstelik kışlık olmadığını iddia etti. Onu götürüp üst kattaki dolaba koymamı istedi.

Ama bu sabah duştayken, okula o deri ceketle gitmenin ne kadar müthiş olacağını düşünmeden edemiyordum. Evden çaktırmadan çıkabileceğimi, geri döndüğümde de ceketi annem fark etmeden dolaba geri koyabileceğimi biliyordum.

Böylece annem Manny'ye kahvaltı yaptırırken, üst kata çıktım, ceketi aldım ve ön kapıdan dışarı süzüldüm.

UÇAK GELİYOR!

ZIP

Öncelikle şunu söylemeliyim: Annem ceketin kışlık olmadığını söylerken haklıymış.

Ceketin astarı bile yoktu. Okula giderken yarı yolda kararımdan pişmanlık duymaya başlamıştım bile.

Eldivenlerim evdeki paltomun cebinde kalmıştı, ellerim de donuyordu. Ben de ellerimi ceketin ceplerine soktum ama her cepte bir şey vardı

Ceplerden birinde çok havalı bir pilot güneş gözlüğü vardı, bu tam bir bonustu. Diğerinde, alışveriş merkezlerindeki fotoğraf kabinlerinde çektirilen fotoğraflardan bir tane buldum.

141

Önce resimdeki insanları tanıyamadım ama sonra bunların annem ve babam olduğunu fark ettim.

Keşke bu resmi kahvaltıdan hemen sonra görmeseydim.

Okula gittiğimde, koridorda yürürken herkes dönüp bana bakıyordu.

Hatta o kadar ilgi çektim ki, ceketi gün boyu üzerimden çıkarmamaya karar verdim. Sınıfta kendimi yepyeni biri gibi hissediyordum.

Dersleri başlatacak zil çalmadan birkaç dakika önce, kapıdaki küçük cam gürültüyle vuruldu.

Bunu yapanın kim olduğunu gördüğümde, az
kalsın kalp krizi geçirecektim.

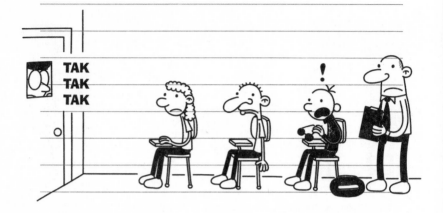

Öğretmen kapıyı açtı. Annem doğruca masama
geldi ve herkesin önünde benden babamın deri
ceketini geri vermemi istedi.

Anneme, havanın eve ceketsiz gidemeyeceğim
kadar soğuk olduğunu söyledim. O da bana
giymem için KENDİ mantosunu uzattı.

Bu durumdan pek hoşnut olmadım. Ama en azından eve dönerken üşümüyordum

Çarşamba

Okulda herkes annesinin zorla kendi mantosunu giydirdiği çocuğu duydu. Bu, dans için kendime eş bulmamı daha da zorlaştıracak.

Bu yüzden ben de dansa bizim okuldan OLMAYAN biriyle gitmeye karar verdim. Ve sanırım bakabileceğim en mükemmel yeri buldum: kilise.

Kilise okulundaki öğrencilerin, devlet okuluna giden çocukların çok sert olduklarını düşündüğünü duymuştum. Bu yüzden, ne zaman arkadaşlarımdan biriyle kilisede karşılaşsam, kilise çocuklarının önünde çok havalı davranmaya çalışıyordum.

Geçenlerde, annem kilisede Bayan Stringer ile arkadaş oldu çünkü ikisi de Sonbahar Kermesi Komitesi'nde çalıştılar.

Stringer'ların kilise okuluna giden iki çocukları var. Wesley adında bir oğlan ve Laurel adında bir kız. Wesley'yi hiç görmedim. Ayin sırasında diğer küçük çocuklarla birlikte bodrumda oluyor herhalde.

BAY   LAUREL   BAYAN
STRINGER   STRINGER   STRINGER

Birkaç akşam önce, annem, bu Cuma akşam yemeği için bütün Stringer ailesini bize davet etti. Manny ve Wesley'in iyi anlaşacaklarını, Manny'nin sonunda gerçek, canlı bir insanla arkadaş olabileceğini umuyor sanırım.

Ama asıl BENİM için bir şans var. Laurel benimle yaşıt ve sınıfımdaki kızların çoğundan daha güzel. Yani bu akşam yemeği benim talihimi değiştirebilir.

<u>Cuma</u>

Annem, Stringer'lar gelmeden önce uzun zaman
harcayıp evde hazırlık yaptı. Etrafıma şöyle
bir bakınca, benim de bazı hazırlıklar yapmam
gerektiğini gördüm.

Her yerde utanç verici şeyler vardı. Bir kere,
Noel ağacımız hâlâ salonda duruyordu. Süsleri
indirmek çok uzun işti; bu yüzden babamla ağacı
öylece garaja götürdük.

Salondaki mobilyaların her köşesine yapıştırılmış
bebek bezleri vardı; Manny emeklemeye
başladıktan sonra, annem evi bebeğe uygun hale
getirmek için yapıştırmıştı bunları.

148

Bezlerin iyi tutması için ambalaj bandı kullanmıştı; bunları çıkarmak da hiç kolay değildi.

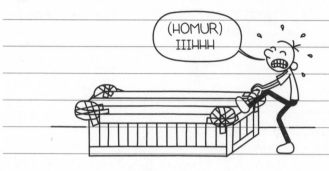

Gary Amca, salondaki kanepede şekerleme yapıyordu. Biz de üzerine bir örtü örttük ve kimsenin oraya oturmak istemeyeceğini umduk.

Sırada mutfak vardı. Mutfakta, üzerinde annemin biz çocuklara yıllardır vermiş olduğu sertifika ve kurdelelerin bulunduğu bir mantar pano var.

Üzerinde benim adımın yazılı olduğu her şey çok sinir bozucu. Ben de panoyu duvardan alıp kilere sakladım.

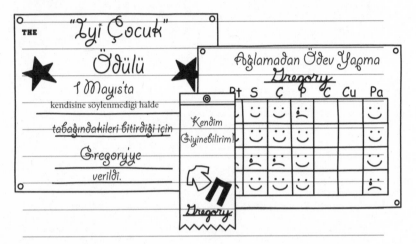

Stringer'lar geldiğinde, işlerin önemli bölümünü halletmiştik. Ama ziyaret çok sarsıcı bir şekilde başladı. Manny'nin okulda vampir gibi davranan bir çocuktan korktuğunu söylemiştim, hatırlıyor musunuz? İşte o çocuğun Wesley Stringer olduğu anlaşıldı.

Böylece, annemin Manny'nin yeni bir arkadaşı olacağına dair umutları suya düşmüş oldu. Manny yemek yemedi ve gecenin geri kalan kısmını odasında saklanarak geçirdi. Ben de bunu yapabilmeyi çok isterdim çünkü annem konukları etkilemek için garip, süslü püslü yemekler pişirmişti.

Üzerinde kuşkonmaz olan kremalı mantarlı tavuk vardı mesela. Kuşkonmazın faydalı olduğunu biliyorum ama bana kriptonit gibi geliyor.

Yine de Laurel'in karşısında şapşal görünmek istemedim; bu yüzden gözlerimi kapamaya, burnumu tıkamaya ve kuşkonmazı yutmaya karar verdim.

Büyükler, politika filan gibi hiç de ilgi çekici olmayan şeyler konuşuyorlardı. Laurel ve ben de öylece oturup dinlemek zorunda kaldık.

Annem, Bayan Stringer'a, babamla "kaçamak" yapmak istedikleri gecelerde gittikleri şık restoranı anlatıyordu. Bayan Stringer, kocasıyla hafta sonları yemeğe çıkamadıklarını, çünkü Laurel'in hep arkadaşlarıyla bir şeyler yaptığını, kendilerinin de Wesley için güvenilir bir bebek bakıcısı bulamadıklarını söyledi.

Bayan Stringer'a, bebek bakıcısına ihtiyaç duyduklarında BENİ çağırabileceklerini söyledim.

Bunun, Stringer'lar ile iyi ilişkiler kurmanın, bir de para almanın bir yolu olduğunu düşünüyordum. Bu fikir annemin de hoşuna gitti ve bebek bakıcılığının benim için harika bir deneyim olacağını söyledi. Bayan Stringer çok etkilenmiş gibiydi. Bana yarın işimin olup olmadığını sordu. Olmadığını söyledim.

Şimdilik haddimi aşan laflar etmek istemiyorum ama bir gün, Şükran Günü'nde, Stringer'lar ile aynı masada oturacağımdan, eskiden, ortaokuldayken kayınbiraderim Wesley'ye nasıl bebek bakıcılığı yaptığımı konuşup hep birlikte güleceğimizden eminim.

Cumartesi
Bu akşam 18:30'da annem beni Stringer'lara bıraktı.

Bayan Stringer, Laurel'in bir arkadaşının evine gittiğini söyledi. Bu çok fenaydı; çünkü Laurel'i birkaç dakikalığına da olsa görebilmeyi ve onunla dans hakkında konuşmayı ummuştum.

Bayan Stringer, Wesley'yi saat sekizde yatırmam gerektiğini söyledi. Kendileri de dokuz civarında evde olacaklardı. Onlar dönene kadar televizyon izleyebilir ve buzdolabından istediğim şeyi yiyebilirdim.

Bay ve Bayan Stringer gittikten sonra, Wesley ile baş başa kaldık. Ona oyun filan oynamak isteyip istemediğini sordum. Ama Wesley, garaja gitmek ve bisikletine binmek istediğini söyledi.

Ona dışarısının bisiklete binemeyecek kadar soğuk olduğunu söyledim ama İÇERİDE binmek istiyordu. Stringer'ların gerçekten çok güzel bir evi var. Wesley'nin parkeleri filan çizmesini istemediklerinden emindim. Bu yüzden Wesley'ye yapacak başka bir şeyler bulmamız gerektiğini söyledim.

Wesley ağlama krizi geçirdi. Sakinleştikten sonra, bunun yerine boyama yapmak istediğini söyledi. Ona boyalarının nerede olduğunu sordum. Çamaşır odasında, dedi. Ancak boyaları almaya gittiğimde, kapının üzerime kilitlendiğini duydum.

Sonra garaj kapısının açıldığını duydum. Biraz sonra, Wesley'nin bisikletiyle mutfakta dolaştığını anlayabiliyordum.

Beni dışarı çıkarması için kapıya vurdum ama oralı olmadı.

Derken bodrumun kapısı açıldı ve bir takırtının ardından müthiş bir çarpma sesi duyuldu. Wesley'nin merdivenlerin altında ağladığını duyabiliyordum. Çok kötü yaralanmış gibiydi; paniğe kapılmaya başlamıştım.

Ama sonra Wesley sakinleşti ve bisikletini merdivenlerin tepesine sürükledi. Sonra bisikleti merdivenlerden aşağı sürdü ve yine yere çarptı. Bu kez DAHA ÇOK ağladı.

Bu bir buçuk saat böyle devam etti, inanın abartmıyorum. Wesley'nin başına bir iş geleceğinden korktum ama gelmedi. Stringer'ların Wesley için bebek bakıcısı bulamadıklarını söylediklerini hatırladım. Bu şimdi mantıklı gelmeye başlamıştı.

Çamaşır odasından çıkar çıkmaz, Wesley'yi kapıyı üzerime kilitlediği için cezalandırmam gerektiğini düşündüm. İyi bir dayağı HAK EDİYORDU: Ama Stringer'lar bundan hoşlanmayabilirlerdi.

Ben de ona oturma cezası vermeye karar verdim. Çünkü küçükken yaramazlık yaptığımda, annemle babam beni hep böyle cezalandırırdı. Hatta küçükken, Rodrick bile oturma cezaları verirdi bana.

Tabii, o zamanlar Rodrick'in bana ceza verme YETKİSİNİN olmadığını bilmiyordum. O bana bakıcılık yaparken, ceza sandalyesinde kaç saat oturmuşumdur, bilmem.

Bir keresinde, Rodrick ile evde yalnızken top oynuyordum. Yanlışlıkla annemle babamın düğün fotoğrafını devirip kırdım. Rodrick de bana bu yüzden yarım saat oturma cezası verdi.

Annemle babam eve geldiklerinde, kırılan çerçeveyi gördüler ve bunu hangimizin yaptığını sordular. Onlara benim yaptığımı ama beni cezalandırmalarına gerek olmadığını, zaten Rodrick'in oturma cezası verdiğini söyledim.

Annem yalnızca anne ve babanın ceza verebileceğini söyledi. Böylece, o çerçeveyi kırdığım için çifte ceza yemiş oldum.

Wesley'nin de beni çamaşır odasına kilitlediği için ÜÇ cezayı hak ettiğini düşündüm. Ama vakit geç oluyordu. Stringer'lar eve döndüğünde, hâlâ içeride kilitli olmamın kötü olacağını düşündüm.

Bu yüzden başka bir çıkış yolu aramaya başladım. Arka tarafa açılan kapının önünde duran bir yedek buzdolabı vardı. Bütün gücümle dolabı ittim ve sığabileceğim kadar bir yer açtım. Sonra da kapıyı açtım.

Dışarısı gerçekten çok soğuktu. Üzerimde yalnızca tişörtüm ve pantolonum vardı. Ön kapıyı açmaya çalıştım ama kilitliydi.

Bu çocuğu hazırlıksız yakalayacaksam, sürprize ihtiyacım vardı. Ben de evin etrafını dolaştım ve birinci kattaki bütün pencereleri denedim. Sonunda bir tane kilitli olmayan pencere buldum. İtip açtım ve eve girdim.

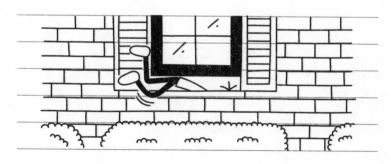

Kendimi birinin yatak odasında buldum.
Etrafıma bakınınca buranın Laurel'a ait olması
gerektiğini anladım.

Söylediğim gibi, dışarısı buz gibi soğuktu. Benim
de Wesley'nin peşine düşmeden önce ısınmam
gerekiyordu. Ama birkaç dakikalığına yatağa
girdiğime çok pişman oldum çünkü ben Laurel'ın
odasındayken, Bay ve Bayan Stringer eve
gelmişlerdi.

Umarım ileride, Şükran Günü'nde bu hikâyeyi de anlatıp gülebiliriz. Ama Bay Stringer'ın bütün bunlara gülebilmesi için aradan biraz zaman geçmesi gerekecek.

Çarşamba

Laurel Stringer ile ilgili şansımı da kaybettikten sonra, dansa götüreceğim birini bulmaktan vazgeçmiştim neredeyse. Dansa yalnızca üç gün kalmıştı ve şimdiye kadar herkes biriyle eş olmuştu. Ben de cumartesi gecesini evde tek başıma bilgisayar oyunu oynayarak geçirmeye karar verdim.

Ama dün, Dans Komitesi toplantısından sonra, Rowley bana her şeyi değiştiren haberler verdi.

Abigail Brown toplantı sırasında çok mutsuzmuş; çünkü dansa birlikte gideceği çocuk, yani Michael Sampson, ailevi sebepler yüzünden onu ekmiş. Kendine çok güzel bir elbise alan Abigail, dansa birlikte gideceği birini bulamıyormuş.

İşte benim sahnem gelmişti; artık bir kahraman olabilirdim. Rowley'e benim yancım olarak kendini göstermesi için bunun büyük bir fırsat olduğunu söyledim. Abigail ile aramı yapabilirdi.

Ancak mesele şu: Abigail beni tanımıyor. Onun tanımadığı biriyle dansa gitmek isteyeceğinden kuşkuluydum. Ben de Rowley'den Abigail'e dansa ÜÇÜMÜZ birlikte, "bir grup arkadaş" olarak gidebileceğimizi söylemesini istedim.

Rowley bu fikirden hoşlanmış gibiydi. Çünkü o da bütün zamanını Dans Komitesi'nde çalışarak geçirmişti ve dansa birlikte gidebileceği kimsesi yoktu.

Üçümüzün yemeğe gidebileceğimizi, restoranda Abigail'in benim ne kadar harika biri olduğumu görebileceğini düşündüm. Dans salonuna gittiğimizde, ikimiz içeri bir çift olarak girebilirdik.

Tek sorun, bizi götürecek birine ihtiyaç duymamızdı. Bunu annemden isteyemezdim, çünkü bizim arabanın koltukları cips kırıntıları ve daha kim bilir nelerle kaplı. Üstelik annemi randevuma götürmem tam bir felaket olabilirdi.

GREG'İN ALTINI BAĞLADIĞIMIZ GÜNLER DAHA DÜN GİBİ!

Abigail'i gerçekten etkilemek istiyorsam, bir limuzin kiralamam gerekirdi ama böyle şeyler insana bir servete maloluyor. Derken aklıma bir fikir geldi.

Rowley'in babasının çok güzel bir arabası var. Ondan bizi götürmesini isteyebilirdik. Abigail'in, Bay Jefferson'in Rowley'in babası olduğunu öğrenmesine bile gerek yoktu. Biz bir şey söylemezsek, onun profesyonel şoför olduğunu düşünebilirdi. Belki de daha da inandırıcı olsun diye, ona şu şoför şapkalarından bile alabilirdik.

Elbette, BAY JEFFERSON'a da bir şey söyleyemezdik. Geçmişte onunla benim aramda kötü şeyler olmuştu. Bana iyilik yapmak için can atmadığından emindim.

Bugün her şey yerli yerine oturmaya başladı. Rowley, Abigail ile konuştu. "Arkadaş grubu" fikri, Abigail'in hoşuna gitmiş. Bay Jefferson da bizi dansa götürmeyi kabul etti.

Şimdi, bugün ile cumartesi arasında her şeyi mahvedecek bir şeyler olmaması için dua ediyorum.

Cuma

Gary Amca'ya danstan söz ettiğimde benden daha çok heyecanlandı. Bütün ayrıntıları öğrenmek istedi. Orada kaç kişi olacak, DJ. ayarlandı mı... filan. Ama bu soruların cevaplarını ben de bilmiyordum çünkü Dans Komitesi'nde olan Rowley ve bunlar onun alanına giriyordu.

Ben daha çok ne GİYECEĞİM üzerinde yoğunlaşmıştım. Gary Amca, eğer yanımdaki kızı etkilemek istiyorsam, takım elbise giymem gerektiğini söyledi. Rodrick'in dolabına baktım ve onun Gary Amca'nın düğünlerinden birinde giydiği takım elbiseyi buldum.

Rodrick'in ıvır zıvır çekmecesinde parfüm
bulamadım ama televizyonda reklamı yapılan şu
vücut spreylerinden buldum. Bunu kullanmak
konusunda biraz tereddütlüydüm çünkü eğer bu
şey gerçekten reklamlarda gösterildiği kadar
işe yarıyorsa, yarın gece kabusa dönüşebilirdi.

Büyük Amca Bruce birkaç yıl önce öldü.
Garajda, içinde onun kişisel eşyalarının olduğu
bir kutu olduğunu biliyordum. Orada bir şişe
parfüm buldum ve önce bileğimde denedim.

Tam Büyük Amca Bruce gibi kokmuştum. Ama
vücut spreyini kullanmaktan daha güvenliydi yine
de.

Babamdan beni markete götürmesini
istedim ve Abigail'e bir kutu Sevgililer Günü
çikolatası aldım. Ama kutunun jelatinini hiç
çıkarmamalıymışım çünkü dayanamayıp fıstıklı ve
karamelli çikolataları kendim yiyiverdim.

Umarım Abigail hindistancevizli ve tadı diş
macunu gibi olan çikolataları seviyordur çünkü
geriye yalnızca onlar kaldı.

Cumartesi
Bu gece Büyük Sevgililer Günü dansı gecesiydi ve
her şey aksiliklerle başladı.

Hazırlanmak için Rowley'lerin evine gittiğimde, onun yüzünde sivrisinek ısırığını andıran kırmızı benekler olduğunu gördüm. Sonra bunların ne olduğunu anladım: SUÇİÇEĞİ.

Evan Whitehead birkaç hafta önce okula suçiçeği ile geldiğinden beri, hastalık sınıfta yayıldıkça yayıldı.

Geçen hafta dört çocuk, okul hemşiresi tarafından eve gönderildi. Bunlardan birinin Deli Şort olduğundan eminim çünkü Salı gününden beri hiç şort indirme vakası olmadı.

Suçiçeğinin SÜPER bulaşıcı olduğunu duydum. Buna yakalanan bir çocuğun bir hafta boyunca okula gelmesine izin verilmiyor. Ama Rowley'in bir GECE bile eve hapsolmasını kabul edemezdim. Onunla dansa gidecektik ve eğer anne babası onun gitmesine izin vermezlerse, benim de gidemeyeceğimi biliyordum.

Rowley'e suçiçeği olduğunu söyledim ama keşke bu haberi ona bir anda değil, alıştıra alıştıra verseymişim.

Rowley hemen aşağı koşup bunu anne babasına söyleyecekti ama ona sakinleşmesini, bunu birlikte halledeceğimizi söyledim.

171

Bu geceyi, hastalığını kimseye haber vermeden atlatırsa, ömrümün geri kalanı boyunca ona borçlu olacağımı söyledim. Yapması gereken tek şey, suçiçeğini örtbas etmek ve anne babasına bir şey çaktırmamaktı. İkimiz birlikte dansa gidecek ve harika vakit geçirecektik. Kimsenin öğrenmesine gerek yoktu ki.

Ama Rowley çıldırmış gibiydi, doğru dürüst düşünemiyordu. Onu sakinleştirip susturmak için iki tane hindistancevizli çikolata vermek zorunda kaldım.

Rowley şimdi suçiçeği olduğunu bildiği için DELİ gibi kaşınıyordu. Ben de çekmecesinden çoraplar alıp ellerine geçirdim.

Rowley'in anne babası suçiçeğinin nasıl bir şey olduğunu biliyor olmalıydılar; benekleri gizlemenin bir yolunu bulmalıydık. Anne babasının yatak odasına gittik ve makyaj malzemelerinin arasında kullanabileceğimiz bir şey olup olmadığına baktık. "Kapatıcı" adında bir şey buldum ve bunun işimize yarayacağını düşündüm.

Çekmecede bulduğum küçük bir fırçayı kullanarak Rowley'in suratındaki sorunlu bölgeleri kapatmaya çalıştım.

Ama Rowley'in makyaj yaptığı hemen anlaşılıyordu. Ben de Bayan Jefferson'ın çekmecesinden ipek bir şal aldım ve Rowley'e bunu takıp ağzının çevresine sarmasını söyledim. Sonra da alnında da suçiçekleri olduğunu fark ettim. Annesinin dolabında bulduğum hasır şapkayı verip bunu da giymesini istedim.

Rowley'in pek normal göründüğünü söyleyemeyeceğim ama en azından suçiçeği olduğu anlaşılmıyordu.

Arabaya bindiğimizde nefesimi tuttum ama sanırım Bay Jefferson, Rowley'in kıyafetinin ortaokula özgü bir tür moda filan olduğunu düşündü ve bir şey söylemedi.

Arabaya binmek için arka kapıyı açtığımda, Rowley'in eski bebek koltuğunun hala arkada olduğunu görüp çok şaşırdım.

Rowley'e babasının arabasında neden hâlâ bebek koltuğu olduğunu sordum. Kendisi normal bir koltuğa oturacak kadar büyüdükten sonra bebek koltuğunu çıkarmadıklarını söyledi. Bu arada düşünüyorum da, Rowley ailesiyle birlikte arabada yolculuk ederken hep gözüme fazla uzun boylu görünmüştü zaten.

Abigail'i almaya gitmeden önce o şeyi çıkarmamız gerektiğini biliyordum çünkü bir limuzin şirketi asla arabasında bebek koltuğu tutmaz.

Ama o şeyi sökebilmek için mühendis filan olmak gerekiyordu anlaşılan. Zaten Abigail'i almaya gitmek için geç kalmıştık. Öylece bıraktık.

Abigal'in evinin önüne geldiğimizde, Bay Jefferson'dan geldiğimizi haber vermek için kornayı çalmasını istedim.

Ama Bay Jefferson korna çalmadı ve bir "hanımefendi"ye böyle muamele edilmemesi gerektiğini söyledi. Birimiz kapıya gitmeli ve ona eşlik etmeliydik.

Rowley arabadan inmeye hazırlandı ama ben bunun Abigail'i etkilemek için büyük bir fırsat olduğunu fark ettim. Böylece eve gidip kapıyı çaldım.

Ama kapıyı Abigail açmadı. Babası açtı. Bay Brown şu motosikletle gezen polislerden filan sanırım. Ya da öyle giyiniyor.

Bay Brown, Abigail'in üst katta olduğunu, hazırlandığını, birazdan ineceğini bildirdi.

Bana içeri girmemi ve beklerken oturmamı söyledi. Abigail'in aşağı inmesini beklerken aradan bir saat geçmiş gibi geldi. Bu arada Bay Brown'un belindeki kelepçelerden de hiç hoşlanmamıştım.

Sonunda bu kadar stresin Sevgililer Günü dansı için fazla olduğuna karar verdim ve oradan sıvışmaya hazırlandım. Ama ben tam çıkmak üzereyken, Abigal merdivenlerden indi.

İlk fark ettiğim şey, Abigail'in çok kabarık bir elbise giydiği oldu. Üçümüzün birden Bay Jefferson'in arabasının arka koltuğuna sığmamız mümkün değildi. Rowley'in bebek koltuğuna oturmam da mümkün değildi; bu yüzden önde oturmak konusunda gönüllü oldum. Üstelik Bay Jefferson'in ön koltukları ısıtmalıydı; bundan da faydalanabilirdim.

Bay Jefferson ön koltuğa bir yığın kâğıt koymuştu. Bizim danstan çıkmamızı beklerken vergi işleriyle filan uğraşmayı düşünüyordu herhalde.

Onca şeyi kaldırmak zahmetli işti; ben de bir an önce geceye başlayabilmek için bagaja biniverdim.

Abigail, Rowley'in çocuk koltuğunda oturmasından pek rahatsız olmuşa benzemiyordu. Bunun bir tür şaka filan olduğunu sandığından eminim.

Ama mizah BENİM işim; Rowley'in benim rolümü çalmasına izin veremezdim.

Arabanın içi sessizleşmişti. Ben de Bay Jefferson'dan radyoyu açmasını istedim. Ama o müzik yerine, sıkıcı konuşmaların yapıldığı kanallardan birini açtı. Yolun geri kalanı boyunca bunu dinlemek zorunda kaldık.

Bunu, kendisine "Şoför" dememe bozulduğu için yaptığından eminim.

Rowley ve Abigail sohbet ediyorlardı. Bense arkada hoparlörlerin hemen yanında oturuyor ve onların ne konuştuklarını duyamıyordum.

Bay Jefferson durunca, restorana geldiğimizi sandım. Ama Bay Jefferson'ın elektrikli süpürgesini almak için bir tamircide durmuştuk.

O anda limuzin için para biriktirmediğime pişman oldum. Çünkü profesyonel bir şoför, restorana giderken yolda canının istediği gibi durmazdı.

BOB ELEKTRİKLİ
SÜPÜRGE TAMİRİ

AÇIK

Annemle babamın hep sözünü ettikleri şık restoran Sprigga'da rezervasyon yaptırmıştım. Bunun biraz tuzluya patlayacağını biliyordum ama ev işleri yaparak kazandığım paraları biriktirmiştim. Çok fiyakalı görünerek Abigail'i etkilemek istiyordum.

Otoparka geldiğimizde, Bay Jefferson inmem için bagajın kapağını açtı. Ama aşağı indiğimde, her tarafıma elektrik süpürgesinin yağlı lekelerinin bulaştığını gördüm.

Pasaklı ve şapşal görünmek istemiyordum. Bu yüzden ceketimi arabada bıraktım ve hep birlikte restorana girdik. Rowley'in anlayışlı davranacağını ve babasıyla geride kalacağını umuyordum. Ama o da bizimle geldi.

Sprigga benim düşündüğümden çok daha şık bir yerdi. İçeri girdiğimizde, bizi karşılayan görevli restoranda erkeklerin ceket giymelerinin zorunlu olduğunu söyledi.

Ama takım elbisemin kirli ceketini giymem mümkün değildi. Ben de görevliye bu defalık bir istisna yapıp yapamayacağını sordum. Yapamayacağını ama restoranda bulunan ceketlerden ödünç alabileceğimi söyledi. Verdiği ceket üzerime çok büyük geldi ama yine de giydim.

Oturduğumuzda, çok kötü bir koku geldi burnuma. Nereden geldiğini anlamaya çalıştım. Derken BENDEN geldiğini fark ettim. Sanırım ödünç aldığım ceket daha önce yüzlerce kişi tarafından giyilmiş ve hiç yıkanmamıştı.

Yemek boyunca bir başkasının pis kokusunu taşımak istemiyordum. Bu yüzden izin isteyip tuvalete gittim. Ceketin koltuk altlarını sabun ve suyla ovdum ve el kurutucusunda kuruttum.

Bu her şeyi daha da BERBAT etti. Isı, pis kokunun daha da yayılmasına neden oldu.

Canıma tak etmişti artık. Abigail ve Rowley'e buranın zibidilere göre olduğunu, çıkmamız gerektiğini söyledim.

Ceketi kapıdaki görevliye verdim. Üçümüz birlikte dışarı çıktık. Yemekten vazgeçip doğruca dansa gidebileceğimizi söyledim. Ama Abigail aç olduğunu söyleyerek karşı çıktı. Rowley de açlıktan öldüğünü söyledi.

Civardaki tek restoran Corny idi. Ama oraya
asla gitmeyecektim. Rowley, Corny'deki tatlılara
bayıldığını söyledi. Bu fikir Abigail'e de hoş
gelmişti.

Rowley'i de yanımıza aldığımıza pişman olmaya
başlamıştım. Çünkü tek yaptığı, Abigail'in
tarafını tutmaktı. Benim fikrim her defasında
reddediliyordu. Ama olay çıkarmak istemiyordum.
Bu yüzden dudağımı ısırdım ve Corny'ye kadar
yürüdüm.

Neyse ki kravat meselesini kapıdan içeri
girmeden son anda hatırladım ve kendi kravatımı
arka cebime tıktım.

Ama Rowley'i uyaracak vaktim olmadı. Bu yüzden onun kravatı Utanç Duvarı'nın kalıcı bir parçası oldu.

Corny tam bir HAYVANAT BAHÇESİ idi. Biz ailece hafta içi gidiyoruz oraya; hafta sonu manzara çok daha farklıydı.

İşin tek iyi tarafı, yanımızda küçük çocuk olmadığı için bizi Çocukların Sokağı'na oturtmamaları oldu. Ama Corny'nin "yetişkin" kısmında da durum pek parlak değildi. İki tarafı birbirinden bir cam ayırıyordu. Biz de bir sürü yaramaz çocuğu olan bir ailenin yanına oturmuştuk.

Garsona yer değiştirip değiştiremeyeceğimizi sorduk. Yüzünü ekşitti ve yemeklerimizi başka bir masaya taşıdı. Ama keşke olduğumuz yerde kalsaymışız; çünkü yeni yer daha da beterdi.

Garsondan ikinci kez yerimizi değiştirmesini istemedim çünkü kızdırmak istediğiniz en son kişi size yemek servisi yapan kişidir. Ben de görüntüyü kapatmak için pencerenin önünde iki menüyü üst üste koydum.

Garson bize mısır cipsi getirdi; Rowley de yiyebilmek için ellerindeki çorapları çıkardı. Rowley suçiçeği olmuşken hepimizin aynı sepetten yememizin iyi bir fikir olmadığını düşündüm; bu yüzden sepeti kendime yakın tuttum.

Rowley ne zaman cips istiyor gibi görünse, ona pipetle bir tane uzatıyordum.

Suçiçeğinin havadan bulaşıp bulaşmadığını bilmiyordum. Bu yüzden Rowley ne zaman konuşsa, kendimi garantiye almak için nefesimi tutuyordum.

Bir ara Rowley geçen yaz başına gelen bir olayı uzun uzun anlattı. Sonuna doğru az kalsın bayılıyordum.

Abigail ve Rowley'e yemeği benim ısmarlayacağımı, bu yüzden ne isterlerse yiyebileceklerini söyledim. Paralarımı saçarak Abigail'e gösteriş yapmaya çalışıyordum.

Ama garson geri geldiğinde, Abigail İKİ başlangıç yemeği birden istedi. Rowley de öyle.

Garson, ağzının çevresindeki şaldan dolayı Rowley'in ne dediğini anlayamıyordu; bu yüzden Rowley şalını indirdi. Ama bunu yaptığında, bir damla tükürük havada uçtu ve benim alt dudağıma kondu.

Tükürük molekülü ağzıma giremesin diye çenemi sımsıkı kenetledim. Sakin görünmeye çalıştım ama içten içe deliye dönmüş gibiydim.

Ağzımı peçeteyle silmek istedim ama peçeteyi yere düşürmüştüm ve uzanıp alamıyordum.
Bu yüzden Abigail'in dikkatinin başka yöne kaymasını bekledim ve dudağımı koluma siliverdim.

Siparişimizi verdik. Ben paradan tasarruf etmek için yalnızca sade hamburger istedim. Abigail, menüdeki en pahalı yemek olan biftekten sipariş etti. Rowley de aynısından istedi; oysa ucuz bir şey istesin diye kaş göz işaretleri yapıp duruyordum ona.

Yemeklerimiz geldiğinde, hamburgerimin içinde marul ve domates olduğunu gördüm. Corny'de siparişleri HEP yanlış getirirler zaten. Marul ve domatesi çıkardım; ama burgerimin içinde mayonez de vardı.

Garson tekrar geldiğinde, ona benim içinde hiçbir şey olmayan hamburger sipariş ettiğimi söyledim. O da bir peçete aldı, hamburgerin mayonezini sildi ve peçeteyi de masanın ortasına bıraktı.

İştahım iyice kaçmıştı. Ama aç OLSAM da, yemeğimi bitirmezdim zaten herhalde. Corny'de tabağınızdakileri bitirdiğinizde, altta hiç anlayamadığım bir resim çıkıyor.

Öylece oturup Abigail ile Rowley'in bifteklerini yemelerini bekledim. Bitirdiklerinde hesabı istemek için garsonu çağırdım.

Ama sonra Rowley ve Abigail tatlı istediklerini söylediler. Ta en başında Corny'ye gelmemizin nedeni, yemekten sonra ikram olan tatlılarıydı. Ama tabii Rowley ve Abigail ekstra para ödemek gereken ÖZEL tatlılardan istediler.

Ayağa kalktım ve garsonu bulup bugünün Rowley'in doğum günü olduğunu söyledim. Çünkü o zaman Rowley'in tatlısından para almayacaklarını biliyordum. Böylece birkaç dakika sonra, garsonlar "İyi ki doğdun" şarkısını söyleyerek geldiler ve Rowley'e bedava pastasını verdiler.

"İYİ Kİ DOĞDUN ROWLEY. MUTLU YILLAR SANA!"

Abigail yine de üç katlı çikolatalı cheese-cake istedi ve iki ısırık alıp bıraktı.

Hesap geldiğinde, ne kadar tuttuğunu görünce gözlerime inanamadım. Cüzdanımdaki bütün parayı harcamak zorundaydım. Hatta çorabımda acil durumlar için sakladığım beş doları bile çıkarmam gerekti.

Garson çorabımdan çıkardığım parayı almadı çünkü biraz ıslaktı; bu yüzden arabaya gidip Bay Jefferson'a beş dolarlarımızı değiş tokuş edip edemeyeceğimizi sordum.

Masaya döndüğümde, Rowley ve Abigail bir sohbetin ortasındaydılar. Bana sanki birbirlerine eskisinden biraz daha yakın oturuyorlarmış gibi geldi.

197

Abigail'i, Rowley'den uzak durmak isteyebileceğini söyleyerek uyarmak istedim ama sonra suçiçeği meselesini öğrenirse dansa gelmekten vazgeçeceğinden korktum.

Üçümüz tekrar arabaya bindik. Bay Jefferson bizi okula götürdü ve kapıda indirdi. Rowley'i sıkı sıkı kucakladı. Abigail, Bay Jefferson'ın profesyonel şoför olduğunu düşünüyorsa, bu ona çok garip gelmiştir eminim.

Dansın teması "Paris'te Gece Yarısı" idi. Dans Komitesi'nin çok iyi iş çıkardığını itiraf etmek zorundayım. Spor Salonu'na Fransa'da bir cadde görüntüsü verilmişti. Üzerinde yiyecek ve içeceklerin olduğu uzun bir masa vardı. Bir de altında çileklerin olduğu çikolata pınarı konmuştu.

Biletlerimizi verip fotoğraf çektirmek için sıraya girdik. Bütün çiftler, Paris manzaralı fonun önünde fotoğraf çektirdiler.

Sıra bize geldiğinde, ben de Abigail ile durdum ve fotoğrafçı fotoğrafımızı çekti. Ama keşke Rowley'in de bizimle fotoğrafa girmek isteyeceğini bilseydim... Buna izin vermezdim.

Paris'te Gece Yarısı
Sevgililer Günü Dansı

DJ bana bir yerden tanıdık geliyordu. Yakından bakınca Gary Amca olduğunu anladım. Bu işi nasıl kapmış BİLMEM.

Gary Amca bunu tişörtlerini sınıf arkadaşlarıma satmak için bir fırsat olarak gördü galiba. Spor salonu karanlıktı, bu yüzden öğrenciler kazıklandıklarının farkında değildiler.

Bir ara Abigail benim yanımda duruyordu, sonra kayboldu. Onu spor salonunun diğer ucunda arkadaşlarıyla konuşurken gördüm.

Yanlarına doğru yürüdüm ama ben oraya varamadan hep birlikte kızlar tuvaletine gittiler.

Kızların neden tuvalete grup halinde gittikleri konusunda hiçbir fikrim yok. Ama bunun ŞİMDİ olması gerilmeme yol açmıştı.

Abigail'in benim hakkımda ne düşündüğünü bilmiyordum. Belki de o sırada arkadaşlarına tam da bunu anlatıyordu. Spor salonunda erkekler tuvaleti kızlar tuvaletinin hemen yanında. Ben de tuvalete girip kulağımı duvara yapıştırdım.

Bir sürü kıkırdama duyuyordum ama erkekler tuvaletindeki gürültüler yüzünden, neler söylediklerini çıkaramıyordum.

FOŞ

İnsanların gürültü yapmalarını engellemeye çalıştım ama faydası olmadı.

Duvarın diğer tarafında sessizlik olmuştu. Ben de spor salonuna geri döndüm. Abigail ve arkadaşları içeceklerin başında duruyorlardı.

Saat 19:50'de Gary Amca müziği açtı. Dans başlıyor gibiydi. Ama o sırada içeri büyükannem yaşında insanlar girmeye başladı.

Saat 20:00'de yüzlerce yaşlı insan girişin etrafında toplanmıştı. Bayan Birch onlarla bir şeyler konuşuyordu. Ben de neler olup bittiğini anlamak için yaklaştım.

Yaşlılar, yeni yapılacak Huzurevi hakkında toplantı yapmak için spor salonunu kiraladıklarını söylediler. Öğretmenlerden biri, Bayan Sheer da onlara kendisinin spor salonunu iki hafta önce bu dans partisi için rezerve ettirdiğini açıkladı.

Ancak yaşlılar kendilerinin AYLAR önce rezervasyon yaptırdıklarını, bunu kanıtlayacak belgelerinin olduğunu söylediler. Sonra da rahat rahat toplantılarını yapabilmeleri için biz çocukların salonu boşaltmamızı istediler.

Ama sonra Dans Komitesi'ndeki kızlardan bazıları araya girdiler ve işler çığrından çıkacak gibi göründü.

Tam herkes kavga çıkacak diye düşünürken, Bayan Sheer bir uzlaşma önerdi. Spor salonunu paravanla ortadan ikiye bölebileceğimizi, yaşlılar bir tarafta toplantılarını yaparken, çocukların da diğer tarafta dans edebileceklerini söyledi.

PARAVAN

DANS

YAŞLILAR EVİ TOPLANTISI

Herkes bu fikri benimsemiş görünüyordu. Temizlik görevlisi, paravanı getirdi.

Salonun yarısını kaybetmemiz kötü olmuştu. Ama esas keyfimizi kaçıran IŞIKLAR oldu. Spor salonundaki bütün lambaları tek bir elektrik düğmesi yakıyor. Yani ışıkların ya hepsinin kapalı ya da hepsinin açık olması gerekiyor. Yaşlılar toplantılarında ışıkların açık olmasını istediler. Bu da salonun bize ait olan tarafında "Paris'te Gece Yarısı" temasının sonu oldu.

Işıkların yanması Gary Amca için de kötü olmuştu çünkü artık çocuklar ondan aldıkları tişörtleri görebiliyorlardı ve kazıklandıklarının farkındaydılar. Paralarını geri istemeye başladılar.

Gary Amca müziği açarak herkesin dikkatini başka tarafa çekmeye çalıştı. Bir sürü kişi dans pistine doluştu.

Kızlar spor salonunun ortasında büyük bir grup halinde dans ediyorlardı. İkide bir oğlanlardan biri dans ederek gruba girmeye çalışıyordu. Ama kızlar oğlanları dışarıda tutmak için duvar oluşturmuşlardı adeta. Kendim çemberin ortasına girmek için hamle yapana kadar bunu anlamadım. Birden önüm tamamen kesildi.

Yaşlılardan biri salonun bize ait olan tarafına geldi; müziğin sesinin çok yüksek olduğundan yakınarak kısılmasını istedi.

Bunun üzerine Gary Amca sesi %80 oranında kıstı. Artık Yaşlılar Evi toplantısında söylenen her bir sözcüğü duyabiliyorduk.

Ancak bu, kızları rahatsız etmemiş gibiydi. Birçoğu, kişisel müzikçalarlarını çıkarmışlar, dans etmeye devam ediyorlardı.

Ancak oğlanların canına tak etmişti. Onca zaman kızların yanında uslu ve kibar davranmaktan sıkılmışlardı. Sonunda dağıttılar.

Bayan Sheer ve diğer gözlemciler çocukları sakinleştirmeye çalıştılar ama durum umutsuzdu. Gerçekten çok acayip bir sahneydi ve durum giderek daha tehlikeli bir hal alıyordu.

Ayak altından çekilmek ve gidip banklara oturmak istedim ama o sırada Deli Şort yeniden ortaya çıktı. Ben de en iyisinin olduğum yerde kalmak olduğuna karar verdim.

Arada bir, dansa yeni gelenler oluyor ve spor salonunda olup bitenleri görünce gerisin geri dönüyorlardı. Ama saat dokuz civarında, Michael Sampson, Cherie Bellanger ile el ele içeri girdi.

Michael, Abigail'in birlikte dansa gideceği çocuktu. Sanırım "ailevi meseleler" hikâyesi tam bir yalanmış.

Yüzündeki ifadeye bakılırsa, Abigail'in de orada olmasını beklemiyordu.

Bundan sonrası tam bir dramdı. Michael kız arkadaşını orada bırakıp kaçtı. Abigail de yarım saat boyunca spor salonunun köşesinde durup gözlerini sildi.

Abigail'in kendini daha iyi hissetmesi için elimden geleni yaptım. Ama etrafında bir kalabalık toplanmıştı, bu yüzden beni fark ettiğinden emin değilim.

O sırada, Yaşlılar Evi toplantısı bitti. Yaşlılardan bazıları bizim tarafa kayıp yiyecek içeceklerimizden faydalanmaya başladılar.

Çilekleri o kadar çabuk bitirdiler ki, insanların çikolata pınarına bandıracakları bir şey kalmadı.

Bunun üzerine çocuklar da parmaklarını pınara batırmaya başladılar. Ortalık Corny'ye döndü.

Çocuklardan biri çikolata pınarının içine kontak lensini düşürdü. Bayan Sheer da herkesin geri çekilmesini, kendisinin lensi pınarın içinden çıkarmaya çalışacağını söyledi.

Toplantı bittiği için, Gary Amca müziğin sesini açtı.

Ancak yaşlılar şarkı isteklerinde bulunmaya başladılar. Biraz sonra Sevgililer Günü dansımıza yaşlılar hakim olmuştu.

Ben de arka duvarın dibinden olup bitenleri izliyor ve bu dansa gelmeyi neden istediğimi düşünüyordum. Aynı zamanda Rodrick'in ıvır zıvır çekmecesinde bulduğum vücut spreyini kullanmadığım için de pişman olmuştum çünkü Büyük Amca Bruce'un parfümü benim yaş grubumun dışındaki insanları çekiyordu.

Saat neredeyse on olmuştu; Gary Amca bir sonraki şarkının gecenin son şarkısı olacağını duyurdu. Müzik çalmaya başladığında, birkaç çift piste çıktı. Gece boyunca ilk kez oluyordu bu.

Şarkının bitmesini sabırsızlıkla bekledim. Çünkü dans tam bir felaketti. Benim de tek istediğim bir an önce eve gidip bilgisayarda oyun oynamak ve bu akşam yaşadıklarımı beynimden silip atmaktı.

Ama tam artık daha kötü bir şey olamayacağını düşünürken, Ruby Bird'ü gördüm. Üzerime üzerime geliyordu.

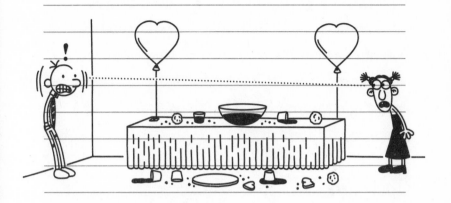

Beni dansa mı kaldıracaktı yoksa onu çıldırtacak bir şey mi yapmıştım bilmiyordum. Ama dans partisinin sonunda ısırılmak istemiyordum.

Kaçacak bir yol aradım ama ayağım takılınca düştüm. O sırada Abigail tuvaletten çıktı. Ben de Ruby'nin yanıma gelmesine fırsat vermeden Abigail'in eline yapıştım.

Abigail'in ağlamaktan makyajı akmıştı. Ama umurumda değildi. Ruby'den kaçmak için bir bahane bulduğuma sevinmiştim. Doğrusunu söylemem gerekirse, sanırım Abigail de beni gördüğüne sevinmişti. Onu dans pistine boş bir alana götürdüm.

Daha önce hiçbir kızla dans etmemiştim. Ellerimi nereye koyacağımı bile bilmiyordum. Abigail ellerini benim omuzlarıma koydu. Ben de kendi ellerimi cebime soktum ama bu biraz garip geldi. Sonra ortada buluştuk ve mesele halloldu sanki.

Derken Abigail'in çenesinde bir şey fark ettim. Tam da Rowley'in suçiçeğine benzeyen kırmızı bir benekti bu.

Şimdi, bundan sonra olanları anlatmadan önce kendimi savunmak için suçiçeğine yakalanmanın eşiğinde olduğumu söyleyeyim.

Ama itiraf edeyim, biraz aşırı tepki vermiş olabilirim.

Ama bunun suçiçeği olmadığı ortaya çıktı. Basit bir sivilceymiş yalnızca. Abigail yine ağlamaya başladı ve makyajı bu kez yanaklarından aktı.

N'apalım... Şimdi bunu biliyorum ama benim yerimde kim olsa aynı tepkiyi gösterirdi.

Ama sanırım Abigail pek öyle düşünmedi. Çünkü geri dönüş yolunda benimle neredeyse hiç konuşmadı.

Abigail'in evinin önüne geldiğimizde, onu içeriye Rowley götürdü. Bana göre hava hoştu.
Ben de böylece çikolataların geri kalanlarını yedim. Geçirdiğim geceden sonra AÇLIKTAN ÖLÜYORDUM.

Çarşamba
Sevgililer Günü dansından bu yana çok şey oldu.

Birkaç gün önce, Gary Amca tişört satarak kazandığı parayla bir sürü piyango bileti aldı ve biletlerden birine kırk bin dolar çıktı. O da babama olan borcunu ödedi, bana "kadınlar" konusunda iyi şanslar diledi ve evden taşındı.

Diğer önemli haber şu: Ben ağır bir suçiçeğine yakalandım.

Hastalığın bana nasıl bulaştığını bilmiyorum ama umarım Rowley'den kapmamışımdır; çünkü Rowley'in vrüslü hücrelerinin bağışıklık sistemime saldırdığını düşünmek hiç hoşuma gitmiyor.

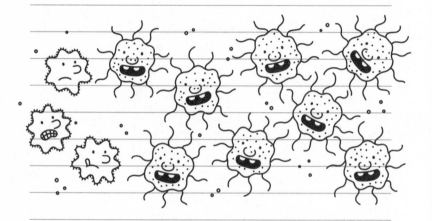

Ama suçiçeğini Rowley'den kapmadığıma eminim. Geçen gün okula giderken gördüm onu, yanağında annesinin boyaları vardı. Belki o kırmızı benekler Abigail'inki gibi yalnızca lekeydi.

Rowley ve Abigail'dan söz etmişken, ikisinin artık bir çift olduklarını duydum. Tek söyleyebileceğim şey şu: Eğer bu doğruysa, Rowley dünyanın en kötü arkadaşı demektir.

En az bir hafta okuldan uzak kalmam ve evden çıkmamam gerekiyordu. İşin iyi tarafı şu: Evde hiç kimse yokken, rahatsız edilmeden uzun uzun banyolar yapabiliyorum.

Ama itiraf edeyim, suyun içinde o kadar uzun süre kalmak hatırladığım kadar güzel değilmiş. Çünkü bir saat sonra derin buruş buruş oluyor. Dokuz ay bunu nasıl yapmışım, hiç bilmiyorum.

Üstelik bütün gün tek başıma olunca kendimi yalnız hissediyorum. En azından yalnız olduğumu sanıyorum. Bugün, küvetin yanına temiz havlu koymuştum. Gözlerimi açtığımda, havlunun yok olduğunu gördüm.

Ya biri benimle dalga geçiyor ya da Johnny Çedar yine iş başında.

TEŞEKKÜRLER

Bana verdikleri destek için ve hep güldükleri için harika aileme teşekkür ederim. Yaşadığımız bütün hikâyeleri bu kitaplara yerleştirdim. Bu serüveni sizinle paylaşmak o kadar keyifli ki.

Kitaplarımı büyük bir özenle yayınladıkları için Abrams'taki herkese teşekkürler. Her kitaba, sanki ilk kitapmış muamelesi yaptığı için Charlie Kochman'a teşekkürler. Greg Heffley'nin başarılı olması için yaptığı için her şeyden dolayı Michael Jacobs'a teşekkürler. Çabaları ve dostlukları için Jason Wells'e, Veronica Wasserman'a, Scott Auerbach'a, Chad W. Beckerman'a ve Susan Van Metre'ye teşekkürler. Birlikte çok güzel zamanlar geçirdik, bundan sonra da geçireceğiz.

Jess Brallier'a ve Poptropica'daki bütün ekibime destekleri, yaratıcılıkları ve çocuklar için yazdıkları harika öyküler nedeniyle teşekkürler.

Muhteşem ajansım Sylive Rabineau'ya rehberliği ve teşviki için teşekkürler. Elizabeth Gabler, Carla Hacken, Nick Dangelo, Nina Jacobson, Brad Simpson ve David Bowers'a Greg Heffley'yi ve ailesini ekrana taşıdıkları için teşekkürler.

Her şeyin kusursuz bir şekilde işlemesini sağladığı ve bana pek çok açıdan yardımcı olduğu için Shaelyn Germain'a teşekkürler.

YAZAR HAKKINDA

Jeff Kinney, *New York Times* çok satanlar listesinde defalarca 1 numaraya yükselmiş çocuk kitapları yazarıdır. *Saftirik Greg'in Günlüğü* serisiyle altı kere Nickelodeon Kids "Choice Award" en sevilen kitap ödülünü kazandı. *Time* dergisi tarafından Dünyanın En Etkili 100 Kişisi'nden biri seçildi. Kendisi aynı zamanda *Time* dergisinin seçtiği en iyi 50 web sitesinden biri olan Poptropica.com'un yaratıcısıdır. Çocukluğu Washington D.C.'de geçen yazar 1995 yılında New England'a taşındı. Halen güney Massachusetts'te eşi ve iki oğluyla birlikte yaşıyor. Burada An Unlikely Story adında bir kitapçıları var.

notion. Clearly, they do not. Can these apparent shortcomings of my analysis be avoided?

These problems dissolve once it is recalled that the conditions for 'the same notion' are labile when applied to an individual. Strict identity is appropriate when comparing community notions, since a community notion is an abstraction and is defined to be exactly indicated by the definition of the term used to express it. Thus, too, it follows that two communities whose definition for a term differs, will have different community notions. Period. Things are different when an individual's notion is compared to either another individual's or to a community's notion; here we must relax the conditions for being the same notion, as exact similarity is not required. Such difference in the construal of 'the same notion' depending on whether or not an individual's notion is in question is supported by two claims that both Burge and I accept: (1) that there is no strict conceptual-factual distinction and (2) that it makes sense to say that an individual has the same notion as do other members of her community, even when she deviates somewhat from them or from the norm of her community. In contrast, it makes no sense to speak of the community's notion deviating from the community's norm. Thus, I am not committed to the claim that the community's notions actually and counterfactually are identical. Thus, the second objection is met.

By adding the following to this last point, I can show how the first objection to my view is also avoided. The counterfactual community intends a certain notion to be associated with their term 'arthritis'. The community's notion is different from ours because the meaning of the word 'arthritis' is stipulated to be different. That is just how community notions and word meanings are related. In important contrast, while Bert in the actual world is somewhat deviant, this is not tantamount to either Bert's *meaning* something different by the term or having a different notion associated with it than does the rest of his actual community. Strict similarity criteria are not applicable in comparing an individual's notion with another individual's, or when his notion is compared with the community's notion. So the community notion associated with the term 'arthritis' differs in the actual and counterfactual cases, and while the community does not have the same notion in both cases, Bert does. Individualism remains unscathed.

8   Minimal Content, Quine, and Determinate Meaning

In previous chapters I argued that ignoring the first-person concept of minimal content led to false results and quandaries regarding the mind. In this chapter I will do the same for language. I will start by introducing several new concepts—concepts that are based upon that of minimal content.

The new concepts are *intended reference, intended interpretation*, and *objective reference*.[1] The first two are first-person concepts; the latter is a hybrid first-person and third-person concept. In spite of their first-person aspects, objective knowledge of intended reference and intended interpretation is possible, as is the case with minimal content. I will demonstrate how these concepts shed light on meaning and reference by exploring how they alter our understanding of W. V. Quine's famous theses of Indeterminacy of Translation and inscrutability of reference. I will argue that without these first-person concepts Quine's thesis of Indeterminacy of Translation is vacuous and reference is nonsense. Quine was aware that reference was at risk of being reduced to nonsense on his view, but he thought he eliminated that risk. I will argue that he failed to protect reference from nonsense, and I will expose the vacuity of Quinean Indeterminacy. (I attempted to show this in my Ph.D. dissertation. At that time I had only a most inchoate idea of minimal content and, thus, certainly no independent support for it. In consequence, my arguments against Quine's theses were not as compelling as they could have been. I believe the earlier deficiencies have been at last corrected in this book.)

Nevertheless, I will argue that there is something of great philosophical importance in Quine's theses of Indeterminacy of Translation and inscrutability of reference, once they are understood in the light of intended interpretation and intended reference. Of course, and alas, these are not alterations of which Quine would approve. In chapter 9 I will argue that consequences of deep significance for ontology and realism result. In this chapter, in anticipation the next chapter, I will introduce a fourth concept: *ontic reference*. It is decidedly not a first-person concept.

The New Concepts

I turn first to an exposition of intended reference and intended interpretation. Help is obtained from Quine's notion of *theory form* and his notion of a *model*:

> We may picture the vocabulary of a theory as comprising logical signs such as quantifiers and the signs for the truth functions and identity, and in addition descriptive or non-logical signs. . . . Suppose next that in the statements which comprise the theory . . . we abstract from the meanings of the non-logical vocabulary and from the range of the variables. We are left with the logical form of the theory, or, as I shall say, the *theory form*. Now we may interpret this theory form anew by picking a new universe for its variables of quantification to range over, and assigning objects from this universe to the names, and choosing subsets of this universe as extensions of the one-place predicates, and so on. Each such interpretation of the theory form is called a model of it, if it makes it come out true. (Quine 1969,[2] pp. 53–54)

This, of course, is just the usual way of obtaining what in mathematical logic is called a formal theory and then considering alternative models for it. The ideas of formal theories and alternative models were utilized in chapter 1 in the discussion of the various number and set theorists. The concept of *interpretation* includes that of *model*, as it drops the requirement that it makes the theory come out true. Thus, all models are interpretations, but not conversely. Those ideas have been applied to languages; here the concept of interpretation is more appropriate than that of a model, as we are concerned with the semantics of sentences regardless of their truth values. Consider a formal language as a vocabulary plus syntax. The vocabulary is a set of sign types specified as an alphabet and a list of primitive "words" (not necessarily recursively specified). The syntax consists of the rules of formation that enable one to construct well-formed "sentences." The syntax, then, will include various functors and punctuation marks. "Words" and "sentences" are enclosed in quotation marks in the preceding since they are not meaningful in the semantic sense since they are elements of a formal language. They become semantically meaningful on specification of an interpretation.

As is well known from Quine's work, changing the interpretations of the individuative apparatus (definite and indefinite articles, plurals, pronouns, identity, and related linguistic items) is central to giving alternative translations of a language, and this is part of the syntax; thus the functors in a formal language are also left uninterpreted. With this in mind, given a meaningful language, we may abstract from it the language form (or formal language) in a similar fashion as Quine indicated for the obtaining of a theory form from a theory. (In fact, to specify a formal theory one must first specify a formal language to express the formal theory.)

The *intended reference* (IR) of a formal expression of some formal language will depend on the interpretation at issue. It is the object or the kind (set) of objects assigned *under some one interpretation*. In the first instance, it will be an individual referring expression, and in the second it is a general referring expression. I will speak of the *intended interpretation* (II), as opposed to the intended reference, when I wish to speak more broadly of a sentence or a language and not just its referential parts. Though II and IR are distinguishable, they are inseparable. The referring parts of language are not separable from the individuative apparatus, hence, not from II. Thus, when I explicitly speak of just one of these it should be understood that the other is implicit. I will often use the abbreviations II and IR not so much for brevity as in the hope of minimizing the possibility of accreting extraneous features associated with the expression 'intended' from the vernacular.

I argued in chapter 5 that for there to be a representation it was essential that a *particular* mapping be employed by (or, when explicit, selected by a conscious agent). I dubbed this the *particularity requirement* and the problem of doing so the *particularity problem*. There is a related particularity requirement for securing a *single* interpretation for a language. We will see that the satisfaction of the particularity requirement for language also requires a first-person perspective, a subjective point of view, and, hence, a conscious agent. The term 'intended' is employed to reflect the role of a conscious agent, as well as the fact that the purported referent is a *particular* object (or a *particular* set of objects); it is not merely any of the several possible referents which a referring term could have if compensatory adjustments were made in the interpretation of the individuative apparatus. That such compensatory adjustments can be carried out is the crux of Quine's theses—this I do not dispute. What I argue below is that Quine's view lacks the resources to handle this "particularity requirement" because he eschews the subjective.

It is important to realize that both of the concepts IR and II have dual and related application: I apply these concepts to both individual agents and language communities. They are generic ways of identifying a *purported* word-world relation for either a particular agent or for a particular community. When the individual's determination of the word-world relation is at issue and the word is a singular term, the IR is specified by the individual's minimal content; when the word is a general term, the IR is the extension of the agent's individual notion. When the community's determination of the word-world relation is at issue, this amounts to questions about the standard extension of the linguistic sign, and it will express either the objective content or the community notion, depending on whether the term is singular or general. In such cases, I speak of the community's intended reference. Of course, an individual agent strives to have her IRs match those of her community's, to be non-deviant. That is one major thing she tries to achieve as she learns the language of her community.[3]

While the concepts of *intended reference* and *intended interpretation* are word-world relations involving either an individual or a community, there is an implicit mind-word relation in these concepts, since they specify *purported* objects via the mapping intended by the individual agent. This last point radically divides me from Quine's view. It also brings out the relation between minimal content and these new concepts that are based on it. The solution of the particularity problem for representation depended on that of minimal content, the subject of a thought as conceived by the thinker. Intended reference is the correlative concept when language rather than thought is under discussion. The concept of intended reference is ultimately rooted in the concept of minimal content, and it plays a similar logical role. When a speaker utters or writes a sentence, there is a legitimate and quite restricted sense in which she constitutes its interpretation. I will explain this restricted sense below; we shall see that the constitution at issue falls far short of constituting meaning. As with minimal content, a speaker non-inferentially knows her IR and her II. The possibility of her being in error regarding which interpretation or reference she intends makes no sense. As before with minimal content, this does not imply that a speaker cannot be wrong regarding what is in the world, nor does it guarantee that her intended reference or interpretation matches that of her linguistic community.

My discussion of what a speaker intends to refer to will for the most part be confined to standard situations; I will not be concerned here with cases of mistakes or slightly deviant uses on the part of the speaker. Not that these are unimportant; Burge-type cases are deviant in this way, and they were discussed in chapter 7. These cases are not, however, germane to the issues surrounding the indeterminacy of translation.

I digress here to explore yet a different kind of mistake, but only to put it aside and to add some further clarity to the notion of intended reference. When a speaker intends to refer to a rabbit (as we and she, being English speakers, would understand the term), but when what prompted her utterance was not what we would call a rabbit but some other kind of creature, we have a case of mistaken reference. Mistakes (and deviant uses), unlike the relevant Quinean cases, can be exposed on behavioral grounds. Consider such a case of mistaken reference: A furry animal scurries by and I say "Did you see how quickly that rabbit moved?" My friend points out that it was not a rabbit but instead a groundhog, and he takes me to a trap in which the animal has (conveniently) been caught. I acknowledge my mistake and say "Well, I thought it was a rabbit, I thought it was one of those"—as I point to a rabbit that has (again, conveniently) been watching us. Here both my friend and I, despite my mistake, have our intended references in line with one another's, and they match our community's notions of *rabbit* and *groundhog*.

In the above situation, the speaker knew what he intended to refer to with his uses of 'rabbit'. Though his individual notion did not deviate from the community's notion, he was mistaken as to what prompted his utterance. This is an ordinary kind of mistake that has no bearing on any ultimate ontological question or any other philosophical issue. When we say he was mistaken, we are not saying that the object in question was *really*, in some ultimate sense, a groundhog, but only that in ordinary contexts the kinds of stimulations that were presented are the ones members of our community, including the speaker, ordinarily associate with the type of object that we call a 'groundhog', not a 'rabbit'. There is inter-subjective agreement that the second object referred to was a rabbit and the first was a groundhog.

This inter-subjective agreement is important. Where there is this agreement on the referent of a term, I will call it *objective reference*. Objective reference is the linguistic analogue to the *objective content* of an agent's thought, introduced in chapter 1; it is also the extension of a community notion (chapter 7). Recall that the objective content indicates the subject an objective observer of the agent would ascribe as the subject of the agent's thought.

In this sense, 'objective reference' pertains to (assumed if not actual) inter-subjective agreement on, to put it in Quinean terms, the parsing of stimulus meanings. Ordinarily, and often philosophically, we uncritically assume that language is public to this extent. That is, when others use words in a manner similar to the way in which I use them, I take them to be intending to state (refer to) what I would intend to state (refer to) by using that sequence of words.[4] Normally, we assume that our intended references and our individual notions match the objective references and the community's notions. In the interest of effective communication, we strive to make them match.

The objective reference of 'rabbit' in English is just the object that most of us *take to be* the cause of the appropriate stimulations (the affirmative stimulus meaning). This notion of reference, then, is the usual *purported* denotation of a referring expression.[5] It encompasses the objects that are ordinarily thought to exist; thus, 'objective' in 'objective reference' turns on inter-subjective agreement; it accords with common practices of making and attributing references to things. We may meaningfully ask whether one's intended reference matches the objective reference in this sense. IR, then, is in part a function of a given speaker (but not completely independent of her community), whereas objective reference depends on the IRs of a community of speakers and expressions. In specifying these concepts of reference, I used the words 'purported' and 'intended' to prohibit any presupposition that one has actually succeeded in referring to objects of a certain sort, i.e., that the objects in the world are really—independent of us, independent of how we parse the stimulus meanings—of the kind we talk about. That is, there is no claim built into the notions *intended reference* and *objective reference* that we are right about the objects in some deep ontological sense.

The latter brings us to another level at which we may be tempted to apply the term 'objective reference,' viz., when we want to say that the object in the world is *really* of a certain sort, independent of any knowing agent, and over and above the fact that we usually take there to be objects of that sort answering to the expressions in question. Here is a strictly ontological use of 'reference' that goes beyond the above-indicated inter-subjective agreement on the propriety of assent to or dissent from sentences under given stimulation conditions. When the expression is used in this way, we are talking, or trying to talk, at the transcendental level. Call this attempted use *ontic reference*.

Intended reference is the root semantic concept; it ultimately depends on the concept of minimal content. The latter is the root mental concept. An individual agent's thought has a minimal content that she may express with some word that in turn expresses her intended reference. Objective reference is a generalization over individuals' IRs of a given language community based on a presumption of identity of IRs from one individual to another, barring evidence to the contrary. It is the extension of either the objective content or the community notion, depending on whether the term is singular or general, respectively. One may move from either intended reference or objective reference to ontic reference by taking the additional step of claiming that the purported objects are the actual objects in the world in some strong ontological sense. Thus, we see how readily what the more traditionally minded philosopher wants to say about ontology—what there *really* is apart from us—is accommodated in the above. What I have said thus far in this chapter does not exclude talking this way. I think it is ultimately meaningless to do so; I will argue this in the next chapter.

Intended Reference and Quine's Theses

Quine would not countenance my notion of intended reference, since it is based on a first-person methodology. Even so, Quine himself is forced to rely on a similar concept, sometimes implicitly and sometimes explicitly. Consider his discussion of suggestions that have been made for tests to determine the divided reference of the infamous expression 'gavagai'. Quine claims that such tests must be unsuccessful because the stimulus meaning is identical for a variety of possibilities. Thus, he concludes, "the purpose (of such tests) can only be to settle what *gavagai* denotes for the native as a term" (1970, p. 181).[6] That is, such tests cannot settle what the divided reference of the term 'gavagai' *itself* is but, as he says, only what it is *for the native*. Talk of the divided reference of an expression "for a native" sounds, at least superficially, like an appeal to some concept very much like that of intended reference. Occasionally, Quine even talks explicitly of intended references; for example, after stating how more than one model can satisfy a given theory form, he says: "Which of these models is *meant* in a given actual theory cannot of course be guessed from the theory form. The *intended reference* of the names and predicates have to be learned rather by ostension or else by paraphrase in some antecedently familiar vocabulary." (*OR*, p. 54; emphasis added)

How are we to understand Quine's use of the locutions 'which of these models is meant' and 'intended reference'? Is it which of these is meant by the *user* of the theory form, or is it which of these does the *theory itself* (interpreted theory form) mean, apart from any users? Is it the intended references of some user of the names and predicates ("for the native"), or is it the intended references of the names and predicates themselves? For Quine—though not for me—these differences amounts to naught. Though Quine avails himself of the concept of intended reference, ultimately he denies that such talk is meaningful.[7] For he says that we can do no better regarding the divided reference of the term for the native than we can for the term itself, as the native's individuative apparatus is similarly subject to the indeterminacy of translation as is the language itself (1970, p. 181).

The obstacle to determining the divided reference of a term arises, on Quine's view, because the individuative apparatus of the language itself is subject to the indeterminacy of translation; I wholeheartedly agree. I also agree that the native's individuative apparatus—when viewed from the third-person perspective and the data Quine has stipulated—is similarly subject to the indeterminacy of translation. The last result trivially follows from the former, for from the third-person perspective and the stipulated data nothing of the individuative apparatus "for the native" is revealed that is not already revealed in efforts to determine this apparatus for the language itself. The most that this shows, however, is that, so long as we are limited within Quinean constraints, one can no more determine the intended references for the native than one can for the terms themselves. It does not establish that there is no intended reference for the speaker distinct from a term's reference. We saw in chapter 1 a number of reasons for accepting the first-person concept of minimal content, as distinct from objective content. But if we accept minimal content, there is no automatic bar to accepting the first-person concept of intended reference that is based on minimal content and is supported by similar relevant data from the first-person case.

Quine is certainly right in saying that the intended references cannot be decided on the basis of the theory form and that appealing to ostension and paraphrase in some antecedently familiar vocabulary cannot resolve this. Of these means of settling the intended references he says:

But the first [ostension] of these two ways has proved inconclusive, since, even apart from indeterminacies of translation affecting identity and other logical vocabulary, there is the problem of deferred ostension. Paraphrase in some antecedently familiar vocabulary, then is our only recourse; and such is ontological relativity. . . . It is thus *meaningless* within the theory to say which of the various possible models of our theory form is *our* real or *intended model*. (*OR*, p. 54; emphasis added)

The problems of ostension and paraphrase do apply when one is trying to determine *another's* IR, but they are purely epistemic problems.[8] To the extent that Quine suggests that one needs to learn one's own intended reference by ostension or paraphrase, he is quite wrong. An individual is not in the position of having to *learn* which interpretation *she* intends, as another observer of her may well have to, and this for exactly the same reasons one is non-inferentially aware of one's own minimal content (chapter 1), as I argue in the next section. Strictly third-person methodologies are misleading on this point, because they impose artificial constraints. They require turning a blind eye to the first-person perspective, so certain concepts and points remain invisible to it.

Deferred Ostension and Paraphrase: Asymmetry of the First-Person and Third-Person Cases

As a result of Quine's refusal to countenance a first-person perspective, he is forced into the artificial position of maintaining that one must learn one's own intended references by ostension or paraphrase *because* that is how we must do it to ascertain *another's* intended references, i.e., from a third-person perspective.[9] The difficulties that arise from deferred ostension and paraphrase are not applicable to the first-person case.

Consider first the case of deferred ostension. If I point to a gas gauge to indicate the relative volume of gas in the tank, I am non-inferentially aware that this is what I am doing and that I am not indicating anything about the gauge itself. Of course I may not be explicitly aware of this in the sense of thinking (quite artificially), while pointing, "I am now pointing to the gas gauge to indicate the relative volume of gas in the tank, and my main concern is the amount of gas, not anything about the gauge, except insofar as the gauge is related to my main concern." But just as I *am aware* of the subject of my thought as I conceive it (my minimal content), I am aware of my intended reference in ostension in the sense that, if asked, I do not have to infer what it is, nor do I have to *learn* it by any subsequent investigation (be it further ostensions, paraphrase, or whatever). Similar results obtain in more abstract cases of deferred ostension. Thus, if I point to a Gödel number, my intended reference being the correlated formula, there is no question *for me* whether I intend to refer to the Gödel number or to the formula; this is not something I must learn, though another may well have to make some queries of me to learn what is my intended reference. Moreover, in each of these cases I can switch back and forth between the intended references (say, Gödel numbers and formulas) and be non-inferentially aware of which I intend to refer to on any such occasion.

The discussions of the battle diagram and theorist D in chapter 1 made the same point at the level of thought. I could contemplate the battle diagram and switch what was signaled by the Xs and Os, or theorist D could have her minimal contents (and hence her symbols) now represent numbers, now sets. Such switching can be achieved without any change in one's overt behavior; so, another would have to make queries of me or D to ascertain this fact. Such queries would no doubt involve ostensions and paraphrase, with all the usual attendant problems. However, neither I nor D must resort to such means, as we know straight out what is represented in such cases. Our awareness in such cases is direct, but from a third-person perspective it is invisible. Quine constrained to a strictly third-person methodology mistakenly thinks that the problems of ostension and paraphrase apply to oneself, as they do to others.

Each of us has a similar special access to our own intended references, but none of us is in this privileged position with respect to another's intended references. When the issue is another's intended references, each of us is in the position of having to learn what they are. Of course, in practical situations there are contextual clues concomitant with the ostensions that aid one in attempting to learn another's intended reference. For example, if I am driving with a friend and she asks me if we have enough gas to arrive at our destination, and I point to the gauge, she may safely conclude, assuming that I am not perverse, that my intended reference is the amount of gas in the tank and not, say, the pleasant blue light of the gauge. We are not, however, here concerned with the extent to which such epistemic problems of another's deferred ostension may be circumvented (dealt with later), but only with the difference in applicability of some of those problems to the first-person and third-person cases.

The asymmetries between the first-person and third-person cases also apply when we turn to paraphrase. For a wide range of cases, if I make an utterance that employs a referring expression, the intended reference of that expression is again something I am aware of without any need for subsequent learning; typically, there are no inferences that I must make based upon the evidence of my behavior. The "something" I speak of being directly aware of is not the object itself, if there is such a thing; that would be ontic reference, and nowhere will I make such a claim. The "something" may not even be the objective reference, as my intended reference may not match the extension of the community notion. Rather, it is the speaker's awareness of what object(s) she takes there to be and to be speaking of when she makes her utterance—that is, the intended object of her referring expression, objective and ontic reference aside. When I make an utterance involving a referring expression, there is no need for me to paraphrase that utterance in "some antecedently familiar vocabulary" to determine what I intended to refer to by that expression. If there were such a need, we would be in a fine fix, for what vocabulary is more familiar to us than the one we have used for years?[10]

Quine, restricting himself to third-person methodologies, focuses on the words themselves. Regarding the words themselves, there is no difference between the first-person perspective and the third-person perspective, even when stimulus meanings and the speaker's behavior is brought into play. As a result, he entirely misses the asymmetries indicated above and thinks the same problems apply to the first-person case as apply to the third-person case. He has a point when one is asking about the references of the words themselves or of another speaker, but the problems of paraphrase and ostension that apply when considering these cases evaporate in the first-person case. The data from the first-person case, argued for in earlier chapters, are perfectly admissible, and they are required to avoid a truncated and distorted theory of mind. We now begin to see that a restrictive third-person methodology also distorts a theory of meaning and reference.[11]

Of course, an individual may have to paraphrase into an antecedently familiar vocabulary to learn what her intended references ought to be for some terms. This happens when she is trying to get the community notion or objective reference of a new (for her) term, or when she becomes aware that her intended reference associated with a familiar word may not fit exactly that of others. (Her individual notion may be somewhat different from her community's notion, as in a Burge-type deviation.) In the first instance, an individual just learning physics, for example, may have to paraphrase terms such as 'force' and 'electron'. But once physics is learned this is no longer necessary unless, as with the second alternative just mentioned, there is a realization that she has not yet got it just right. But Quine, in making the above claims, is not restricting his attention to sophisticated new terms or to somewhat deviant cases; he is including the most mundane terms, such as 'rabbit'. In any case, once the speaker is adequately educated, she is immediately aware of her intended references—that is, of the objects she is purporting to talk of in making her utterances (regardless of whether there really, in some ultimate sense, are such objects, ontic reference). This awareness is achieved without recourse to ostensive definition or paraphrase.

I am not suggesting that in learning one's first language one has all one's intended references in mind, and that all one has to do is learn how to express them with the linguistic marks of one's language community. Surely there is a complex interplay between the (rudimentary) thoughts of an individual learning her first language and the language used by the community in which she finds herself, an interplay that continues in complex thought processes throughout her adult life. (Compare the case with 'electron' above, or my discussion of sophisticated concepts in chapter 7.) This is not the kind of learning that is in question. Even though Quine sometimes considers this sort of situation, his purpose is not to make any point about actual language acquisition but about meaning.[12]

I conclude, then, that the statement "The intended reference of the names and predicates have to be learned rather by ostension or else by paraphrase in some antecedently familiar vocabulary" (OR, p. 54) is false when applied to oneself. Even so, Quine is right to raise the problem of deferred ostension and paraphrase regarding the determination of another's intended reference, though subsequently I will show that the situation is still not quite as bad as Quine would have us think even in this instance. Once intended reference in my sense is admitted, there is objective evidence that counts toward determining which of the interpretations is intended by another.[13] Still the important point now is that the alleged indeterminacies arising from deferred ostension and paraphrase do not materialize in the first-person case of intended reference and interpretation.

Quine's Quandary, Reference Frames, and the Problem of Particularity

Quine's efforts at making sense of reference in the face of indeterminacy of translation and the inscrutability of reference can succeed only if intended interpretation is introduced, notwithstanding the fact that II is not determinable by strictly third-person methodologies. So much the worse for such methodological scruples as applied to meaning and reference, and so much the better for II, IR, and the root mentalistic concept of minimal content.

After arguing for indeterminacy of translation and inscrutability of reference even as applying to oneself, Quine says:

> We seem to be maneuvering ourselves into the absurd position that there is no difference on any terms, interlinguistic or intralinguistic, objective or subjective, between referring to rabbits and referring to rabbit parts or stages; or between referring to formulas and referring to their Gödel numbers. Surely this is absurd, for it would imply that there is no difference between the rabbit and each of its parts or stages and no difference between a formula and its Gödel number. Reference would seem now to become nonsense not just in radical translation but at home. (*OR*, pp. 47–48)

Quine goes on to give two different ways of rescuing reference from this quandary: one involves the notion of a background language, the other that of a reference frame or a coordinate system. The former purports to give sense to expressions in the object language by paraphrase or description in the background language. The reference-frame approach does not involve an appeal to another (background) language; rather, it involves taking the words of the language in question "at face value." Thus, there is in general a difference between making sense of reference in terms of background languages and doing so in terms of frames of reference or coordinate systems. The differences in these two approaches are later reflected in the "theoretical" and "practical" resolutions of the problem of infinite regresses of background languages.[14]

Reference in the background language, Quine argues, can itself be made sense of only relative to yet another background language, which in turn requires yet another background language, but "in practice we end the regress of background languages, in discussions of reference, by acquiescing in our mother tongue and taking its words at face value" (*OR*, p. 49). While the theoretical resolution (of the problem of infinite regress) comes from a relational theory of what the objects of a theory are, "it makes no sense to say what the objects of a theory are, beyond saying how to interpret or re-interpret that theory in another . . . no ultimate sense in which that universe [i.e. of some theory] can have been specified" (*OR*, p. 50). In short, we must paraphrase in another language. I argue that on Quine's own terms neither the former nor the latter succeeds in rescuing reference from nonsense.

Consider the frame-of-reference approach. Quine writes:

[Picture] us at home in our language, with all its predicates and auxiliary devices. This vocabulary includes 'rabbit,' rabbit part,' 'rabbit stage,' 'formula,' 'number,' 'ox', 'cattle'; also the two-place predicates of identity and difference, and other logical particles. In these terms we can say in so many words that this is a formula and that a number, this is a rabbit and that a rabbit part, this and that the same rabbit and this and that different parts. *In just those words.* This network of terms and predicates and auxiliary devices is . . . our frame of reference, or coordinate system. Relative to it we can and do talk meaningfully and distinctively of rabbits and parts, numbers and formulas. (*OR*, p. 48)

On the frame-of-reference approach, we have that, relative to our frame of reference, we "can and do talk meaningfully and distinctively of rabbits and parts, numbers and formulas" (*OR*, p. 40); we can do so by "acquiescing in our mother tongue and taking its words at face value" (*OR*, p. 49). But what is it, on a Quinean view, to take words at face value? For light on this, let us look again at an excerpt from the passage just quoted:

In these terms [i.e. within English] we can say in so many words that this is a formula and that is a number, this is a rabbit and that a rabbit part, this and that the same rabbit, and this and that different parts. *In just those words.*

Granted, one can *say* these things, use "just those words," but to do so is of no help if those words do not have some particular meaning and reference. The appeal to the locution 'just those words' will help only if the expressions 'rabbit' and 'rabbit part', in English, have their usual denotations, viz., rabbits and rabbit parts. Then, and only then, can *those words* be used to express a *particular* difference.

When we concentrate just on sequences of words uttered under various (verbal and non-verbal) stimulatory conditions, ignoring any subjective states of those who utter the words, this is truly to give the expressions a life of their own. But we then find, given the indeterminacy of translation, that there are no unique answers to what expressions themselves refer to. They can be said to refer to any of a number of different kinds of things so long as appropriate adjustments are made elsewhere in the language. But this is precisely why the reference-frame approach that Quine offers will not eliminate the quandary over reference, for, as was observed earlier, we can assert a difference between rabbits and rabbit stages, in "just those words," only if those words have a particular (at least a purported particular) reference. But how is this to be done on a Quinean view? If the "words" are words qua elements of a formal language, they are meaningless. (My first efforts to develop this point against Quine's views appeared in my thesis (1974). Yalçin (2001) develops this point independently; unlike me, he does not exploit the first-person perspective.)

The point is that the *face value* of the words cannot be the sign or phonemic types, for as marks or sounds they clearly do not and cannot fix any interpretation. So it must be "words" as they appear in some *particular interpreted* language. But how are we to know *which* interpretation—which, so to speak, face value? How is a particular interpretation to be fixed so that the expression 'the face values of words' is significant? In my discussion of representation (chapter 5) there was a problem similar to the one just entertained. There I dubbed it *the problem of particularity*. I use the same locution for the current manifestation of the problem. My contention is that the Quinean view fails to provide the resources to solve this problem. This ultimately undermines Quine's efforts to rescue reference from nonsense on the frame-of-reference approach.

Given the indeterminacy of translation, the words themselves have neither particular meanings nor references—*words themselves have no face value.* The different phonemic or inscriptional types are neither necessary nor sufficient to secure differences of meaning or reference, and Quinean strictures prohibit an appeal to my first-person concept of intended reference (or, more generally, that of intended interpretation). Intended interpretation does provide the resources to meaningfully talk of the "face value of words": the usual denotations and meanings that are associated with the expressions via the intentions of the speakers of the language on a *given* interpretation. From a first-person perspective we know that a particular interpretation can be fixed in one's own case, which one is intended by the agent, though this is invisible from a strictly third-person perspective of the agent. From the latter perspective, it could be any of the permissible alternatives established by Quine. Thus, without II (IR), the face value becomes any of a number of values, *but no one in particular.* Quine's appeal to the "face value" of the words is either empty (as when a formal language is at issue) and of no use to the problem at hand, or it is a disguised appeal to objective reference (in my sense), but the latter is ultimately based on the first-person concept of intended reference. Thus, the face value of words is secured at the price of abandoning a strictly third-person methodology. Quine's unwillingness to pay this price results in his failure to make sense of reference using the "reference frame approach."[15]

One may well point out that the reference-frame approach—taking words at face value—is, for Quine, the practical resolution of the problem over reference; at least this is what he says of the approach when applied to the problem of infinite regress. Admitting intentional idioms to this extent would be acceptable for Quine, since he acknowledges the practical utility of the idioms in question (cf. Quine 1960,[16] p. 221). I have argued that it is more than that, and I will now add to that argument: Quine cannot get off so easily.

I have argued that, with inscrutability and indeterminacy and without intended interpretation, the expression 'take words at face value' is empty. I now reinforce this result by examining what Quine takes there to be involved in knowing a word. Presumably, knowing a word is both necessary and sufficient for being able to take a word at face value. Quine claims there are two parts to knowing a word: (1) a phonetic part—being familiar with the sound of it and being able to reproduce it, and (2) a semantic part— which he explains as knowing how to use it (*OR*, pp. 27–28). These two conditions do obtain in the mother tongue—e.g., for the word 'rabbit', I am familiar with its phonetic component and I know how to use it. Quine tells us that this is sufficient for my knowing the word. Does it provide a basis for taking words at face value so as to resolve the quandary over reference just considered? No. It is sufficient for knowing the syntactical features of a word, but reference is more than that. The *use* of a word is in large part a function of the theory or language *form* where it finds its home and not that of the various interpretations; otherwise different interpretations could not be used for the same language form without behavioral detection. According to Quine, I do not know when I use (correctly) the word 'rabbit' whether I am speaking of rabbit stages, undetached rabbit parts, or rabbits. Use does not discriminate these possibilities. Importantly for Quine, my utterances could be construed as any one of these *without altering the use of the term 'rabbit'*. Thus, the conditions on *knowing the word* that Quine presents cannot help solve the problems lately raised. They do not fix a face value for a word. Here is another way to see the last point: We all recognize that the properties of rabbits are different from the properties of rabbit stages, and that what is true of one is not, in general, true of the other. But if 'rabbit' may be construed as referring to either of these different kinds of objects, certainly *we must take the inscription type 'rabbit' as a different word type under one construal than it is under the other*—the analytical hypotheses would be different. (All this is so in spite of the fact that phonetically and typographically it is the same word and no behavioral criterion would distinguish the different construals.) Since the conditions stated for knowing a word are not sensitive to these different construals, they are not sufficient for knowing a word. The alleged "face value" is ultimately no semantic value on the Quinean view. Quine's discussion of the "face value" of a word does not resolve the quandary over reference—it evades it.[17]

The last point stands even if I am dead wrong about intended reference. All that was needed for the above is the realization that distinct alternatives are required and the indeterminacy of translation. Thus, neither taking words at face value nor appealing to reference systems is sufficient, within Quinean constraints, to save reference from nonsense. It is insufficient because within Quinean constraints the notion *taking words at face value* cannot solve the particularity problem. We have seen, though, that once we allow IR we may then meaningfully speak of the face value of expressions, and that only then can the reference-frame approach be used to extricate us from the quandary over reference that issued from other quarters. Thus, a Quinean must either accept IR or provide another reading of 'taking words at face value'—one that does not presuppose IR. Of course, acceptance of IR also implies the rejection of the indeterminacy of translation applying to oneself, the rejection of first-person indeterminacy. Alternatively, a Quinean could stand fast, reject intended interpretation, and—implausibly—simply hold that reference *is* nonsense.

Quine's Quandary, Background Languages, and the Problem of Particularity

Let us now examine whether Quine's reliance on a background language fares any better in rescuing reference from nonsense. First notice that any background language will itself be indeterminate in precisely the same way as is the object language; i.e., alternative denotations and interpretations for the expressions of the background language will also be possible, any one of which would accommodate all speech dispositions and not be contradicted by any of all possible stimulations, and thus would be equally legitimate. Thus, the background language itself requires interpretation in some background language and similarly for the latter. This Quine explicitly recognizes and labels "the problem of infinite regress." Waiving this problem and keeping the background language fixed—still, if we are to make sense of reference, it cannot be achieved by appeal to a (fixed) background language *within* which we may formulate several incompatible models *and for which it makes no sense to say we mean (intend) one particular model rather than another.*[18] I stress that having multiple models is not, in itself, the devastating blow to making sense of reference in this way. I argue that reference is nonsense only if we go further and deny we can mean (intend) or be aware that we mean (intend) one of these interpretations as opposed to the others. Once the latter is done, as Quine does (the inscrutability and indeterminacy applying to oneself), Quine's attempt to save reference from nonsense fails. For as long as one does not know in terms of *which* of the possible models in the background language the object language is to be paraphrased—and, again, one does not with indeterminacy and inscrutability as applied to oneself—then one has not succeeded in giving a particular meaning and reference to the object language.

Let it not be thought that what is here being argued is merely that Quine's appeal to a background language to make sense of reference merely postpones difficulties; again that is just the problem of infinite regress, and I waived that problem. Rather, I argue that not even a postponement is achieved. What Quine has done by appealing to a background language is purport to resolve (and relativize) the indeterminacy of the object language to a background language; but even assuming that the given background language is fixed, *more than one model can be formulated within it that is an adequate interpretation of the object language*, and since he has precluded our first-person awareness of *which* is intended, *no resolution is achieved—not even relatively*. Once again, the particularity problem has exacted severe damage.

Obviously, if what I have argued in previous sections is correct, one cannot hope to appeal to the "face value" of the formulated model to resolve this problem. What is involved here is one aspect of the doubly relative character of ontology (*OR*, pp. 54–55). That is, we need to know which background language the object language is relativized to and also how the object language is to be interpreted into the given background language—that is, in terms of which model. What has been said above pertains to the second aspect. (In fact, the same problems apply to the first aspect too, in addition to the infinite regress problem acknowledged by Quine, but, as I have said, I put that aside.)

To extricate ourselves from this manifestation of the *problem of particularity*, we need to be able to meaningfully single out, intend a *particular* model among those that we may formulate in the background language and which satisfy the object language. Without this the quandary remains; merely specifying a theory form is, for reasons already indicated, not sufficient.

My contention here is even stronger than any I have advanced thus far: The very notion of an *alternative* translation is itself *without sense* unless we have intended interpretation. Given the indeterminacy of translation, if I can conceive or speak of two or more alternatives, then I must be able to differentiate one from the other beyond their different orthographic or aural types. I must be able to intend one of them as opposed to another, to intend one of them in particular. Without this capacity, the very meaningfulness of talk of two or more alternatives (beyond alternative phonemic or inscriptional types) is lost. To say that some translation is a possible alternative is to say that *that particular* translation is an alternative. But if that translation T can equally be taken as some allegedly different translation T' *and we do not know which is which*, then how can we even conceive of T and T' as different alternatives? (Compare chapter 5, where the problem of particularity played a similarly crucial role in my discussion of representation.) If we take seriously Quine's indeterminacy of translation and inscrutability as *applying to oneself*, one can never be assured that when she speaks of T (interpreted, say, as a "thing" translation) she is not speaking of T' (interpreted, say, as a "stage" translation) and vice versa; indeed the very cogency of saying that we are talking about T rather than T' is brought into doubt. Indeed, the case is worse than just indicated, for a locution such as 'interpreted as a "thing" translation', as used above, would not even be available. These considerations force the conclusion that indeterminacy of translation without intended interpretation is simply vacuous.

Earlier I argued that Quine presupposes and makes implicit use of something like the idea of IR or II. If I am right in the above, he *must* do so for his theses to even make sense. Of course, Quine may avail himself of locutions regarding speakers' intentions or meanings as a practical matter, which he claims to do on several occasions. I am not criticizing his view on the ground that he avails himself of the vernacular for practical reasons. My criticism concerns whether his theoretical formulation of his theses can be sustained without the deployment of some first-person concepts. If what I have argued is correct, this cannot be done; but since he excludes first-person concepts from his theoretical formulation of his theses of indeterminacy of translation and the inscrutability of reference, the status of these are uncertain at best. I maintain that this, coupled with some additional augmentation, shows both that the thesis of Indeterminacy of Translation is vacuous and that reference is nonsense on his view.

To make some of this more concrete, consider another example of Quine's implicit use of intended interpretation in his discussion of alternatives. In discussing an exchange between an immaterialist and a materialist, Quine says the following: "When we come to the immaterialist and we tell him there is a rabbit in the yard, he will know better than to demur on account of a known holophrastic relation of stimulus synonymy between our sentence and some sentence geared to his different universe." (OR, p. 99) And later he says that the immaterialist would agree with our statement about a rabbit in the yard "just to convey agreement on the stimulus content or even out of habit carried over from youth" (OR, p. 103). But if the immaterialist did not think that the materialist intended to refer to something other than what he himself intended, there would be no question of his demurring from our statement regarding a rabbit.

It is clear that unless the materialist and the immaterialist knew their own intended references, knew what they each intended to refer to and thought that it was different from what the other is (probably) purporting to refer to, these quoted passages would be utterly without significance and could have no point, for the materialist in uttering 'rabbit' could equally "mean" (with appropriate adjustments elsewhere) *rabbit stage*, and similarly for the immaterialist. Such first-person shifts in intended references would not be ascertainable from a third-person perspective and are not allowed by the Quinean methodology We have already seen that appeals to just the face value of the phonemic or inscriptional types are of no avail if a difference in semantics is to be secured. The expression themselves cannot fix the semantics; they themselves have no face value. The only option to fix a particular interpretation appears to be the intentions of the agent(s) using those marks or sounds. This, in turn, requires that the agent know her intended interpretation. None of this is possible without augmenting Quine's methodology with a first-person one. Without concepts based upon this expanded methodology, Quine's discussion of the interchange between the materialist and the immaterialist would be nonsense.

What sense is there in speaking of a rabbit (thing) language if one cannot distinguish—even for oneself—intentions to refer to rabbits from rabbit stages? What sense would there be to the dispute between the materialist and the immaterialist if neither intended a particular interpretation of her utterances, and if the expressions themselves lacked particular (semantic) face values? What is being said does not require that one actually be able to correctly determine another's intended interpretation, but only that she has one and it is available to her, from her first-person perspective. At the same time, I recognize that neither one's own nor another's II is behaviorally determinable, nor is it determinable from any strictly third-person methodology. My argument is that our first-person perspective assures us that we each have an II when we use language and there are reasons for thinking we know another's. (I will examine the grounds for objective knowledge of another's II in a later section.)

What is important to secure the meaningfulness of talk of alternative interpretations is a speaker's ability to intend a particular interpretation. Intended interpretation is required for the expressions to have some semantic face value and to solve the problem of particularity. I repeat and stress that it is only *which* interpretation that is determined or constituted by the agent—she does not thereby determine meaning or reference.

Alternative Interpretations, Genuine Hypotheses, and the Vacuity of Quinean Indeterminacy

Perhaps Quine would view the above-mentioned difficulties of fixing a particular interpretation with equanimity, for, as I have already noted, he sometimes suggests that there is in fact no difference between possible translations. Let us examine this claim further. Quine states that "two systems of analytical hypotheses are, as whole, equivalent so long as no verbal behavior makes any difference between them; and, if they offer seemingly discrepant English translations, one may again argue that the apparent conflict is a conflict only of parts seen out of context" (*WO*, p. 78). Thus, for Quine, the alleged alternative translations are *not genuine alternatives*; because as a whole they are empirically equivalent, they are not really different. They appear to be different when we look at individual sentences; however, when we look at the total corpus, the differences, Quine tells us, disappear.[19] Indeed, Quine claims, this result "helps to make the principle of indeterminacy of translation less surprising . . . [it] requires notice just because translation proceeds little by little and sentences are thought of as conveying meanings severally (*WO*, p. 79). It would follow from this not only that the indeterminacy of translation would be "less surprising" but that it would be non-existent—there would *only be an illusion of indeterminacy* so long as the translation was incomplete.[20] All the alternatives would amount to on this view would be alternative systems of linguistic forms (verbal or written). Similarly, the alleged ontological alternatives would not, insofar as they go beyond the empirical content provided by the method of stimulus classes, be genuinely different alternatives. For with respect to just their empirical content, provided by the method of stimulus classes, they are equivalent. Thus, again, all we would have is alternative phonemic or inscriptional forms. But with regard to *these*, there can be *no indeterminacy*, as the differences in phonemic or inscriptional forms *show* themselves. This, however, could be the "face value" only in a trivial and empty sense.

From a theoretical point of view, the Indeterminacy of Translation would be vacuous. Claims to the effect that one does not know what another (be he a foreigner or a neighbor) means and refers to, or that one does not know such things with respect to oneself, lose all effect. With no genuine semantic differences between alternatives, there is then nothing to mean and refer to, save the stimulations that count as the empirical evidence that Quine allows. At best, these claims may be viewed as a misleading way of putting the point that individual sentences do not have meaning *and* that the *only* meaning systems of sentences have lies in their empirical content as determined by the method of stimulus classes.

This point about the content of individual sentences, familiar from Quine's "Two Dogmas of Empiricism," continues in his discussion in "Ontological Relativity" of the empiricist's treatment of statements about the external world. Having gone through the failures of trying to deduce such statements from sensory evidence and logico-mathematical auxiliaries, and the weaker attempt of just translating truths about the world into the latter, Quine tells us that the empiricist concedes that "the empirical meanings of typical statements about the external world are inaccessible and ineffable" (*OR*, pp. 78–79). The explanation Quine offers for this inaccessibility and ineffability is simply that "the typical statement about bodies has no fund of experiential implications that it can call its own" (*OR*, p. 79).[21] Sentences have meaning and experiential implications only by virtue of being contained in a larger theory or language.

To say the latter, however, is not to say that the meaning of sentences is exhausted by the stimulations—those stimulations are compatible with the theory or language as a whole. That is, it does not follow that a sentence—as part of a larger theory or language—does not itself have a particular intended interpretation and reference. It may still, in virtue of the individual's or language community's intention, have some particular interpretation and, thus, say something about particular objects other than stimulations. This is so even if *what* it says is not ultimately separable from the rest of the theory (interpretation) or does not itself, apart from the language of which it is a part, have a separate fund of empirical content. So the meaning holism appealed to, which I endorse, does not preclude particular meaning and reference of individual sentences that are embedded in the language.

Quine's claim that these alternatives are equivalent is closely related to the view that the analytical hypotheses are not genuine hypotheses. To make this out, Quine contrasts analytical hypotheses with hypotheses about stimulus meanings. He takes the latter to be genuine hypotheses. The matching of stimulus meanings, he tells us, is an objective matter:

'Gavagai' and "There's a rabbit"[22] have stimulus meanings for the two speakers, and these are roughly the same or significantly different, whether we guess right or not.

Not so for analytical hypotheses:

. . . no such sense is made of the typical analytical hypothesis. The point is not that we cannot be sure whether the analytical hypothesis[23] is right, but that there is not even . . . an objective matter to be right or wrong about. (*WO*, p. 73)

Clearly, if we preclude the possibility that a speaker intends his utterances to be construed in some particular way, there is nothing to be right or wrong about in constructing analytical hypotheses so long as they conform to the method of stimulus classes. I have already argued against this, but Quine wishes to preclude this possibility, and thus his denial that analytical hypotheses are genuine is not surprising. This reinforces his claim that the alternatives are equivalent, for "so long as no verbal behavior makes any difference between them" *and* there is no intended interpretation we would have no grounds, behavioral or otherwise, for distinguishing them. I conclude (once more) that if Quine is right in holding that the appearance of alternative translations is just a result of "parts seen out of context," and that there is no objective matter concerning which "grand synthetic" analytical hypothesis is the correct one for a given speaker or language community, then not only is indeterminacy of translation "less surprising," as he holds; it is vacuous.

Evidence from the first-person perspective establishes the falsity of a claim that denies that an individual can intend a particular interpretation (or, at the very least, it poses a problem for the claim, a problem that cannot be simply dismissed without begging the question). Once this is acknowledged, we can generalize over the IRs (IIs) of members of the language community to ground a particular interpretation for that community, which we can get right or not. Errors are possible regarding another individual's IR (II) or the generalization over the community. But if there is IR (II), then there is the possibility of getting it right. There is a fact of the matter.

An Answer to a Quinean Counter

Quine marshals seven causes to explain why some fail to appreciate his claim that there is no objective matter to be right or wrong about regarding the choice among workable sets of analytical hypotheses. My arguments to the contrary may be viewed as closely tied to the reason he considers to be the major cause for such failures (the fourth); an examination of this cause may be instructive. I quote at length:

[There] is a stubborn feeling that a true bilingual surely is in a position to make uniquely right correlations of sentences generally between his languages. This feeling is fostered by an uncritical mentalistic theory of ideas: each sentence and its admissible translations express an identical idea in the bilingual's mind. The feeling can also survive rejection of the ideas: one can protest still that the sentence and its translations all correspond to some identical even though unknown neural condition in the bilingual. Now let us grant that; it is only in effect his private semantic correlation—in effect his private implicit system of analytical hypotheses—and that is somehow in his nerves. My point remains; for my point is then that another bilingual could have a semantic correlation incompatible with the first bilingual's without deviating from the first bilingual in his speech dispositions within either language, except in his dispositions to translate. (WO, p. 74)

Does this support Quine's view as opposed to mine? I think not. In fact, given a plausible assumption that I will identify below, this passage supports my view and counters Quine's. What I have said about intended interpretation allows that two bilingual individuals could have different intended interpretations (that is, different correlations), yet neither bilingual will deviate from the other "except in his dispositions to translate." If I had argued that the expressions themselves had some unique interpretations, independent of the person that uses them, then this case would count against that claim, but that has never been my position.

According to me, it is important to realize that there are two ways to understand the question "Is there a *correct* translation?":

(1)   Do the words themselves have a unique meaning and reference?

(2)   Does the speaker, in making utterances, intend them to have some unique meaning and reference?

I agree that Quine's bilinguals show us, as does the indeterminacy of translation, that the answer to (1) is negative. Quine thinks that the second question is based on confusion or false presuppositions regarding meanings, but neither the case of the bilinguals nor indeterminacy of translation establishes this.

Quine, overly impressed by the startling fact that he has uncovered, namely that we cannot distinguish the alternative translation manuals using a strictly third-person methodology, concludes they are not really different.[24] Unable to determine in this way which alternative is the correct one, he gives up on the idea of there being a correct translation manual. In doing so he either ignores (2) or conflates it with (1), a tendency on his part noticed earlier. Either way, it is a mistake that can only be justified by heavy-handed application of a strictly third-person methodology.[25]

When Quine says "there is a stubborn notion that we can tell intuitively which idea someone's sentence expresses, our sentence anyway, even when the intuition is irreducible to behavioral criteria" (Davidson and Hintikka 1969, p. 304), his intent is clear; it is that we are mistaken in persisting in this stubborn notion. But in defending an affirmative answer to (2), I have nowhere argued that one can tell *intuitively* which idea someone else's sentence expresses, and I certainly have not argued that one can have privileged access to someone else's intended interpretation. I have argued that in the first-person case one is non-inferentially aware which interpretation ("idea") one's own sentence expresses. (Whether or not one counts the latter as "intuitively" telling in one's own case is irrelevant.) Quine, without doubt, would not see this as an improvement and, therefore, could not abide an affirmative answer to question (2). I do not rehearse my arguments for that claim here. My present point is simply that Quine's bilinguals do not show us that he is correct here; indeed, they indicate that he is quite wrong on one side of this issue, the one that pertains to (2) above. Here is why: If two bilinguals have different semantic correlations, and their correlations are realized in their nerves, as Quine suggests, then we would have every reason to expect that these neuronal realizations would themselves be different from one another. This is the plausible assumption alluded to earlier. In view of what was developed in chapter 4, they would be manifested by two different dynamical transitions to different attractors in the bilinguals' brains.[26] Not only would this support the claim that each bilingual intended a particular interpretation; in addition, given a fully developed neuroscience, we could determine that they were different by examining their brains.[27] Indeed, we can consider a single bilingual who alternates between translation manuals, as our number theorist D (in chapter 1) did between models for sets and numbers. When the bilingual intends a "thing" translation, his burst states would be different than when he intends a "stage" translation. In any of these cases, that there is one burst state rather than another would clearly be an objective fact of the matter, determinable from a strictly third-person perspective. What one could not determine from this perspective is *which* manual or model the instanced burst state is correlated with; thus, third-person indeterminacy is preserved.

Nothing that I have said opposes indeterminacy of translation as applied to another; thus, correlating the bilingual's 'rabbit' utterances with certain types of her burst states and 'rabbit stage' utterances with different burst states of hers could not settle which is which for her, nor does this conflict with anything I have said. On the arguments I advanced in chapter 4, I hold that which interpretation is intended is realized in the brain of the bilingual as certain burst states, and that different interpretations are realized by different bursts. That a particular burst state occurs in *her* brain, that *she has it*, is what enables the first-person perspective that makes her non-inferentially aware of which manual is operative at the time. This is an additional fact at the level of intentionality that parallels the additional fact at the phenomenal level argued for in chapter 3 (the Mary case). As before, analyzing these burst states from a strictly third-person perspective does not reveal these additional facts.

Quine's denial that there is a correct answer, and the consequent denial of II, follow from his claim that the indeterminacy of translation applies to oneself (first-person indeterminacy), for this implies that one is not aware which interpretation one intends. If there were no data supporting the contention that one is aware of intended interpretation in one's own case, one would be hard pressed to make the case for it. Surely, there would then be no reason to think that one's neighbors had it. But the claim that the inde-terminacy of translation applies to oneself blatantly disregards the first-person data, and it already presupposes that there is no such thing as intended interpretation. Thus, that thesis could not be used as a basis for rejecting II without begging the question. I have already argued that with-out intended interpretation the thesis of indeterminacy of translation is vac-uous. I conclude that there is no first-person indeterminacy of translation.

Meaning over and above an individual's overt behavior is, of course, something Quine would like to banish. I have argued of late that the Quinean framework itself requires some intentional notion, in its theoreti-cal and not merely in its practical formulation, if indeterminacy of transla-tion is not to be vacuous and reference is not to be reduced to nonsense. Thus, despite Quine's desires, the intentional notion of II is required. It is worth repeating that adopting the concept of II does not make *meaning* determinate in one's head, though *which* meaning is thus determined.

Intended Reference, Mentalism, and Privacy

Once the concepts of intended interpretation and reference are deployed as essential elements of an underlying theory of mind and language, there are consequences that appear to conflict with two further central and related proposals of Quine's—proposals that many others who endorse an exclu-sively third-person methodology would support:

(1)   a rejection of any form of mentalism in semantics

(2)   a rejection of any sort of private language.

I will examine the degree of mentalism my theory introduces into seman-tics and whether it brings in its wake a private language.

With respect to (1), Quine says the following:

[With] a naturalistic view of language and a behavioral view of meaning, what we give up is not just the museum figure of speech. We give up an assurance of deter-minacy . . . according to the museum myth . . . the meanings of the words are sup-posed to be determinate in the native's mind. . . . When on the other hand we recognize . . . that "meaning . . . is primarily a property of behavior,"[28] we recognize that there are no meanings, nor likenesses, nor distinctions of meaning, beyond what are implicit in people's dispositions to overt behavior. (*OR*, pp. 28–29)

The primary objection persists even if we take the labeled exhibits not as mental ideas but as Platonic ideas or even as the denoted concrete objects. Semantics is vitiated by a pernicious mentalism as long as we regard a man's semantics as somehow determinate in his mind beyond what be implicit in his dispositions to overt behavior. (*OR*, p. 27)

Quine's reliance on a strictly third-person methodology is, of course, the basis for these remarks.

Independent of Quine, I have made a case for the first-person concept of minimal content and for intended reference, the consequences of which are in direct opposition to Quinean scruples. Of course, I am not denying that behavior also plays a prominent role with regard to meaning. Having said that, I need not argue as to whether the role behavior plays is of such a magnitude as to make meaning "*primarily* a property of behavior," for aside from this quibble there remains an immense difference between Quine and me.[29] My theory—in a specific restricted way—is resolutely committed to regarding "a man's semantics as somehow determinate in his mind beyond what be implicit in his dispositions to overt behavior." Thus, according to Quine, I am committed to a "pernicious mentalism." While I enthusiastically embrace the commitment of my theory to the very limited "mentalism" required by the concepts of intended reference and interpretation, I categorically reject the charge that it is "pernicious."

First, any mentalism involved in my theory is a direct result of the fact that IR and II are first-person concepts. I have argued extensively for the necessity of augmenting any third-person methodology with such concepts for the study of mind and language. Second, the reason that I say that this mentalism is limited regarding semantics is that it is only required to determine *which* reference or meaning, not reference or meaning itself. This limited mentalism is of the utmost importance, for, among other reasons, it solves the particularity problem in its various manifestations, and it saves the Indeterminacy of Translation thesis from vacuity and reference from nonsense. It is imperative to realize that the notions of IR and II do not force us to identify reference or meaning with anything mental, nor have I made any attempt to do so. What I hold is much simpler: What is fixed in the mind(s) of the language user(s) is just *which* interpretation (semantics) she is deploying. This is quite different from holding that the *interpretation* or *semantics* is itself determined in the mind. This is the limited mentalism and the resulting determinacy that IR and II yield.

But do acceptance of the first-person concepts of IR and II and the limited mentalism that such acceptance entails commit us to a private language?

Whatever publicity there is to language on a Quinean view is a result of stimulus meaning, or more broadly, the method of stimulus classes, which also includes dispositions to overt behavior. The method of stimulus classes is a strictly third-person methodology. This serves as a constraint on the permissible analytical hypotheses, though not a sufficiently strong constraint, as Quine himself argues, to determine uniquely a single translation manual. With this I agree; nevertheless, analytical hypotheses must be introduced, for central to Quine's theses is the point that the method of stimulus classes and dispositions to behavior is inadequate for determining the divided reference of terms; indeed, we cannot even determine that an expression is a term without analytical hypotheses. Moreover, there is no avoiding analytical hypotheses, for to speak of "language" without including referring terms would be a severely mutilated and inadequate sense of 'language'; thus, Quinean or not, we must go beyond stimulus meaning and, thus, beyond strict publicity provided by the method of stimulus classes.

It is easy to see that, whatever publicity stimulus meaning provides, we still have when intended interpretation is introduced. This is so because II pertains to the *choice* of analytical hypotheses—not the range of possibilities, but *which one* is operative. Stimulus meaning is a constraint on the range of possible choices for Quine and for me; it operates as a constraint independent of the speaker's choice, her intended interpretation. Still, the difference between Quine's theory and mine on intended interpretation is huge and has already been noted: I allow, while Quine denies, the significance of questions as to which theory or set of analytical hypotheses an individual intends. There is on my view the possibility of getting it right. Whatever "privacy" there is on my theory, it is limited to this "which question" and, therefore, to the limited mentalism that I have argued for.

In concluding this section, let us consider the following passage:

What [indeterminacy of translation] does occasion . . . is a change in prevalent attitudes toward meaning, idea, proposition. . . . [But] a conviction persists, often unacknowledged, that our sentences express ideas, and express these ideas rather than those, even when behavioral criteria can never say which. This is why one thinks that one's question 'What did the native say?' has a right answer independent of choices among mutually incompatible manuals of translation (Davidson and Hintikka 1969, p. 304).

Whether II would reinstate proposition, idea, and meaning I have not determined. I have been careful to stress that intended interpretation *does not constitute meaning or reference*, however these are ultimately construed. The conviction that persists for me is not the one that Quine opposes, namely that our sentences express ideas. Rather, it is that our sentences do express some particular interpretation but they do not do this on their own. Whether they express one interpretation rather than another is determined by an individual's mental act, or by a generalization over such mental acts of the members of the speech community, inferring that they generally intend the same interpretation. Indeed, the very idea of an alternative interpretation requires intended interpretation, as I argued above.

Whatever "privacy" of language there is on my theory concerns *which* interpretation the speaker intends; importantly, this is directly known from the first-person perspective. This is a far cry from holding that there is a private language of the sort that Wittgenstein and others have objected to. The only objection that could be raised against it is that it requires something other than a strictly third-person methodology. Certainly, I have addressed such concerns. I believe that I have laid them to rest.

Objective Knowledge of Another's II or IR

There is some empirical room, and certainly some logical room, for doubt as to the identity of intended interpretation from speaker to speaker; still, there is evidence that may be utilized in attempting to determine a neighbor's II (IR).[30] Given (a) that language is propagated by imitation and feedback, (b) the syntactic isomorphism of another's utterances and one's own, (c), our common culture, and (d) our common biological makeup, it is plausible to suppose another's II is the same as one's own, barring evidence to the contrary. The objective character of (a)–(d) gives reason to hold that we can have objective knowledge of another's II, once the first-person reasons are recognized for holding that there is II in one's own case. If I am aware that I have it, there is no positive reason to deny it to others. The concepts of II and IR are based on that of minimal content. Once we have minimal content, there is no credible reason to deny II and IR. But then there is every reason to suppose that others must have it too, and, just as we have reason to think that we can have objective knowledge of another's minimal content, so too can we have objective knowledge of another's II or IR.

Of course Quine would recognize neither minimal content nor II. Restricting what can count as objective data to the method of stimulus classes, he takes the inability to determine what another's II is on the basis of this method as reason to reject the idea of another's having an intended interpretation. He then goes much further: If another has no II, then I do not either, since if I had II, *another* utilizing a strictly third-person methodology could not determine what it is. It would follow on his view that I would have a private language, but Quine excludes the latter. So, he concludes, neither oneself, nor another has intended interpretation.[31] This reasoning is of a piece with rejecting first-person methodologies.[32] Quine has got things seriously reversed.

Having passed the heady days of old Vienna, why would one think that all that is objective, all there is, and all that is significant, is what can be determined in the strict way that Quine recommends? Claims about one's neighbor's intended interpretation are empirical claims that go beyond one's own experience. As with any other such claims, we can do nothing but base them on the best possible evidence. The theoretical possibility that your neighbor's intended interpretation is different from your own cannot be denied, but this is slim reason to preclude its existence. It certainly is no reason to ignore what is manifestly present from the first-person perspective. Moreover, in the face of the objective reasons provided by (a)–(d) above, it is a good conjecture that not only is another's II typically the same as one's own, such judgments are objective.

Knowledge of a foreigner's II (IR) is not as straightforward as the case of a neighbor's, given the absence of (a), (b), and possibly (c). Though any foreigner can be relatively confident that each of her neighbors has the same II as she does by considerations precisely analogous to the preceding, our relation to a foreigner differs from our relation to one another. For us to obtain knowledge of her II (IR) we would have to construct various tests, e.g., of the kind alluded to in "On the Reasons for Indeterminacy of Translation." Quine does acknowledge that such tests may provide "an indirect hint as to which of various analytical hypotheses regarding . . . [the individuative apparatus] . . . might in the end work out most naturally."[33] I submit that it would be in keeping with good scientific practice (objective empirical research) to take the "naturalness" of the translations guided by these indirect hints as grounds for claiming that the resulting divided references are the ones intended by the foreigner, i.e., the divided reference for-the-native, and correlatively, a certain interpretation of other native linguistic constructions.

Notice that I used 'practice' rather than 'practical' above. Though practical considerations sometimes play a role in science, the doing of science is not itself practical. Thus, when I say that it is in keeping with good scientific practice to base our conclusions about a foreigner's intended references on such evidence, I am not saying, as Quine might, that from a practical point of view we may project certain intended references to the native, even though she does not, in a strict sense, have them. That is, I am not saying that it is merely convenient to speak *as if* the native had them. Rather, I am claiming that the foreigner *does indeed have intended references*, just as my neighbors and I do, and we are doing the best we can to determine what they are, though we may be wrong. The evidence supporting most claims in science is indirect. It is just so for determining another's II, be she foreigner or neighbor.[34] This is no reason to deny the existence of instantiations of first-person concepts, particularly when the first-person data are compelling in one's own case and when their denial leads to unacceptable consequences. Once II and IR are admitted, there is no reason to deny that we can have objective knowledge of them, whether it be one's own, one's neighbor's, or a foreigner's II and IR.

Summary Comparison of the Two Methodologies

The methodological difference between Quine and me is stark. Quine rejects the idea that the translation relation is objective *because* it is indeterminate in principle relative to the totality of speech dispositions. More generally, the translation relation is indeterminate relative to all evidence obtainable from any strictly third-person methodology. On the other hand, once the methodology is expanded to include the first-person perspective, as I recommend, the translation relation is readily determinate in the first-person case, is recognized as objective (in my expanded sense of chapter 3), and is determinable in the case of another (modulo the usual empirical uncertainties in such matters).

Quine, however, holds that the translation relations that I endorse are themselves of no scientific value: "Such postulation promises little gain in scientific insight if there is no better ground for it than that the supposed translation relations are presupposed by the vernacular of semantics and intention." (*OR*, p. 29) If the only basis for such relations were the vernacular of semantics and intention, this would be slim justification for the position.

I have not relied on the vernacular. I have offered different and important reasons for incorporating subjective intentional idioms for the philosophical study of mind and language. First, I have independently argued for the existence of first-person awareness of minimal content and that recognition of such awareness is necessary for an adequate account of mind. Minimal content is the foundation for IR and II. Second, I have shown that successful talk of particular interpretations and the ability to rescue reference from nonsense require—without appeal to the vernacular—intended interpretation. Third, and in consequence of the latter, I have argued that without intended interpretation the Indeterminacy of Translation is vacuous. Fourth, I have shown, using Quine's own example of the bilinguals, how different semantical correlations could be reflected in different objective facts of neuronal conditions in the speaker's brain. (Though from a third-person perspective we could detect the difference, we could not determine which is which.) It follows, then, that we must allow that analytical hypotheses are genuine hypotheses. The alternatives are not semantically equivalent, and the speaker does intend her utterances in some particular way. Fifth, I have given a general argument (in chapter 3 and in the last section of chapter 5) that the use of a first-person methodology in these matters does not diminish the objective character or the scientific nature of the findings. I have applied that reasoning to knowledge of another's intended interpretation. Sixth, since which interpretation a speaker intends is invisible using a strictly third-person methodology, a very limited but innocuous "privacy of language" is allowed.

Which methodology should be adopted? According to my arguments, without incorporating the first-person perspective one cannot meaningfully talk of *particular* interpretations, and without this, Indeterminacy of Translation is vacuous and reference is nonsense. These consequences of Quine's methodology, together with the independent support for the expanded methodology earlier advanced should, I hope, make the choice clear.

One last important general conclusion remains to be made explicit. If what I have argued is correct, it follows that:

1.   The *very idea* of a *particular* interpretation requires the idea of an agent determining this one rather than that one.

2.   The agent's act of determination is itself constitutive of *which* interpretation is at issue.

3.   An agent can non-inferentially know his own particular intended interpretation, his II, but others cannot know his in this way

4.   When someone tries to determine another's II, the thesis of the Indeterminacy of Translation comes into play.

When we add the seemingly uncontroversial assertion that the meanings of sentences of a language are a function of the particular interpretation of the sequences of marks or sounds of the language, and when we recognize that 1–3 decidedly turn on the subjectivity of the agent, it follows that *meaning itself is ultimately grounded in the subjective.*

9　Ontology Downgraded All the Way

I have argued at length against Quine's claim that there is no correct answer as to what an individual intends to refer to or which interpretation she intends. Nevertheless, I wholeheartedly endorse his ingenious arguments as to how compensating adjustments in the individuative apparatus of a language can yield competing alternatives of references and interpretations—alternatives that are neither discriminable by the method of stimulus classes, nor by any strictly third-person methodology. My objections have not been directed against this last point, which I accept. I have argued that intended reference and interpretation are required so that the thesis of Indeterminacy of Translation is not vacuous and reference is not nonsense. Once these concepts are introduced, the consequences of the Indeterminacy of Translation and the inscrutability of reference are different than Quine thought. Among other things, there is no first-person indeterminacy, though third-person indeterminacy remains. I argue in this chapter that even when these theses are understood in light of intended interpretation and reference, there remain very deep consequences for ontology.

Indeterminacy of Translation and Transcendental Metaphysics

There is a crude but informative picture of mind, language, and the world that I wish to exploit. It is crude because I do not enumerate the numerous qualifications that would have to be made for the picture to be accurate. It is informative because even without the qualifications it highlights certain salient and uncontroversial relations between mind, language and the world. The simple picture turns on the fact that language may be used to convey an agent's thoughts and to indicate items or states of affairs in the world—language points to the mind and it points to the world. My purpose in presenting this crude picture is to make explicit a possible ambiguity in the thesis that the Indeterminacy of Translation applies to oneself. I call this *first-person indeterminacy.*

First-person indeterminacy may be construed as the claim that it ultimately makes no sense to hold that an individual intends one translation as opposed to some other, seemingly different one when the two translations are empirically equivalent, since there is no fact of the matter regarding which of the two is the correct translation of the speaker's utterances. This is Quine's position, against which I argued in the previous chapter. But since Quine's thesis of the Indeterminacy of Translation is closely linked with the inscrutability of reference and with his thesis of Ontological Relativity, there is a distinctly different way of reading the claim that indeterminacy applies equally in the first-person and third-person cases: An individual is in no privileged position regarding the determination of which of the possible alternative translations of her utterances *is the one that matches or corresponds to what and how things are really in the world*, no matter how determinately she non-inferentially knows which is her intended interpretation. On this second construal, I will argue that there is no fact of the matter and that differences between first-person and third-person perspectives are, unlike the case for the first construal, nonexistent.

The claim that some one translation describes the way the world actually is would be not only an (interpreted) word-world relation; it also would be an attempted transcendental application of the translation. The term 'ontic reference' was introduced for just such purposes. If we were to speak of transcendental objects, then we might as well speak of their relations and properties and, thus, of transcendental uses of whole sentences. I mark such uses with the locution 'ontic interpretation', which is analogous to 'ontic reference'. Ontic interpretation and ontic reference are equally indeterminate from one's own point of view as from another's. It does follow from Quine's arguments that there is no asymmetry of the first-person and third-person perspectives regarding which translation matches or corresponds with the way the world "really" is. Each of the acceptable translations divides the reference of terms differently. Thus, the objects qua objects purported to be in the world are different for each translation manual, their respective references go beyond the stimulations, and they cannot be uniquely determined on that basis. The reason for this lack of unique determination is that the individuative apparatus of a language is not immune to the indeterminacy of translation and, so, we have the extraordinary consequence that reference or extension is no better off than meaning or intension. Quine tells us that the indeterminacy of translation "began as a challenge to likeness of meaning. . . . Of two predicates which are alike in extension, it has never been clear when to say they are alike in meaning and when not . . . Reference, extension, has been the firm thing; meaning, intension, the infirm. The indeterminacy of translation now confronting us, however, cuts across extension and intension alike. . . . Reference itself proves behaviorally inscrutable." (*OR*, p. 35)[1] He goes on to explain (same page) why extension or reference has seemed to be "firm": Within our own language we think of the apparatus of individuation as given and fixed.

The last point is pertinent to a central result of my theory. On my theory there is an important ambiguity in the use of the terms 'reference' and 'extension'. By the 'extension' or 'reference' of a term we may legitimately indicate (i) the intended reference, (ii) the objective reference, or (iii) the ontic reference.[2] Why these ambiguities are not normally noticed may be explained by the fact that typically when 'extension' or 'reference' is used it is in a context where the operative understanding corresponds to what I have called objective reference. The latter has built into it inter-subjective agreement among members of the community. Moreover, since objective reference is a generalization over the intended references of members of a community with a presumption of identity, there is typically no reason to distinguish intended from objective references in such contexts. Add to this the fact that Quine observed, namely, that the individuative apparatus is normally presumed fixed, and there is no reason to think that intended and objective reference can come apart; hence, typically no reason to distinguish them. Add further the realist tendencies of many philosophers, and there is an implicit presumption that objective reference is ontic reference.

If one accepts Quine's argument to the conclusion that the indeterminacy of translation applies to our home language and accepts my arguments for introducing and distinguishing three senses of reference, then the practice of ignoring the differences is unacceptable. In light of this, consider a famous passage: " . . . the inscrutability of reference is not the inscrutability of a fact; there is no fact of the matter" (*OR*, p. 47). Having discussed three notions of reference, I will examine this claim as applied to each of them.

First, is it true of intended reference? This is basically a mind-word relation, and insofar as my arguments are sound we do have first-person awareness of intended interpretation and, a fortiori, of intended reference; thus, there is no inscrutability of intended reference in one's own case, no first-person inscrutability of reference (nor of intended interpretation). With respect to another person, the case is different, but since there is support for hypotheses about another's intended reference there is no inscrutability of another's IR.[3] Therefore, intended references are not inscrutable in either the first-person case or the third-person case. I have, in effect, already considered Quine's claim at the level of objective reference in discussing the claim as applied to IR in the first-person and third-person cases, for objective reference is just the generalization of intended reference over the speakers of a language community with a presumption of identity. If each speaker has intended reference, then we are right or wrong in presuming an identity of these across speakers, and there is a fact of the matter for objective reference that is not inscrutable. Things are quite different for ontic reference and ontic interpretation; with regard to these, there is no fact of the matter.

The reading of the claim that the thesis that the indeterminacy of translation applies to oneself that I do not accept is the reading in which this claim is understood in the transcendental way: The translation matches or corresponds to the way the world "really" is. So understood, however, it is compatible with the admission of intended interpretation and first-person determinacy regarding it. For certainly an individual's being aware—in a privileged way—of which translation she intends (her II), does not help her (or anyone else) in the least in determining whether that interpretation characterizes the world as it actually is, even when there is inter-subjective agreement on the II of the language within a community. Ontic reference or interpretation concerns an (interpreted) word-(ultimate) world relation which is cognitively and epistemically well beyond that of objective reference.

My case for first-person determinacy regarding II (IR) does not imply anything like an Aristotelian intuition of real essences. What we directly know is which interpretation each of us intends, hence, too, what our own intended references are. We certainly do not thereby directly know which, if any, interpretation fits the world (beyond the stimulations), and certainly not the ultimate ontology; moreover, there are no indirect means to favor one over another, as there is in the case of determining another's intended interpretation or reference. Therefore, we cannot know how the world is in any ultimate sense. With II the relation between mind and language is at issue; the world comes in only indirectly as what the agent thereby *purports* there to be in the world.

IR and II do not imply, and should not suggest, any special powers of the mind to grasp (alleged) ultimate objects, true essences, properties, or relations of things in the world, even in the ordinary sense of things. It is perhaps the belief on Quine's part that the alternative to a naturalistic view of language (as he conceives this) is an intuition of real essences, in some Platonic or some non-abstract realm, that drives him to his excesses. Once the different senses of reference and interpretation that I have introduced are recognized, we see that we need accept neither intuition of real essences nor first-person indeterminacy and inscrutability of intended interpretation and reference. On the other hand, Quine's claim that "the inscrutability of reference is not an inscrutability of fact; there is no fact of the matter"— when understood at the level of ontic reference—is a claim I wholeheartedly endorse. No first-person perspective comes to the rescue here. The objects we usually talk about are *merely* the results of *our* parsing the stimulus meanings, somewhat arbitrarily, if Quine is to be believed, in one of several theoretically possible ways, and that is the best we can do.

Now, one might want to maintain, with Quine, that the method of stimulus classes cannot in principle adjudicate between competing ontologies (as I do), while still maintaining that there are determinable objects in the world independent of us (as I do not); we just cannot determine what they are, and thus separating the epistemic from the ontological matters. That would be to say that although it is a fact that such and such objects exist and that there are facts about these objects (i.e. the properties they have and the relations they stand in) there are ultimate limitations in principle on our knowledge of these things and facts, and hence to claim an epistemic inscrutability of fact but to allow that there is some ultimate fact of the matter.

The previous paragraph would appear to leave open the *possibility* of there being a fact of the matter, of there being objects in the world, even if we are in principle precluded from knowing what they are. I think this is a mistake. Such claims that depend upon the epistemic/ontic distinction presuppose that we can speak of objects in the world independent of any theory or background language, i.e. objects, on the one hand, and theories about them, on the other. I think Quine is right when he denies this: Our talk of theories and ontologies must be relative to a "background theory with its own primitively adopted and ultimately inscrutable ontology" (OR, p. 51).[4] But if it is not possible to speak of objects apart from theories, then there can be *no significance* to talk of ontology apart from a background theory.[5] If this is so, then it also would make no sense to hold that the limitations discussed above are *merely* epistemological.

It is at the level of ontic reference that inscrutability of reference cuts deepest, however, through the bone, as it were. In contrast to the cases of intended and objective reference, there is no evidence as to ontic reference, what objects "really" exist (as opposed to certain acceptable alternatives), and we cannot even talk of objects apart from background theories. Importantly, with regard to ontic reference there is no asymmetry of access between the first-person and third-person perspectives, as there is with intended reference. It is that asymmetry that ultimately allows us to hold that there is a fact of the matter with respect to the correct translation, which interpretation is intended by a given speaker, and what are her intended references. Thus, I reject first-person indeterminacy under the first construal above. But since there is no asymmetry of access to ontic reference, no talk of objects apart from their background theories, and no Aristotelian intuition of "real essences," the inscrutability of reference can bring into doubt the very significance of talk of ontic reference and should lead us to deny that there is a fact of the matter at this level. Thus, I endorse first-person indeterminacy under the second construal above.

Exactly what Quine's position is on the epistemic/ontic issue is confusing, however. There is, on the one hand, his stark claim that "the inscrutability of reference is not an inscrutability of fact; there is no fact of the matter." Quite apart from his point that ontology is always relative to a background theory, this unqualified, bold statement certainly would suggest that he is not merely making an epistemic claim and that he is rejecting ultimate ontological claims. On the other hand, there is the vexing fact that he frequently makes statements that endorse realism. This ambivalence is partly responsible for obscuring the devastating consequences of his ingenious arguments for traditional ontology. Instead of embracing the latter, he repeatedly and persistently endorses a certain kind of realism.[6]

As I see it, Quine erred on both sides of the "double directedness of language." He erred in thinking that there is no correct answer regarding which translation or reference a speaker intends, as I have argued in the previous chapter, and he erred in thinking that his position is compatible with realism, as I argue in the remaining sections of this chapter. I will detail the tension between Quine's avowed realism and his view of ontology and show that the more defensible view is the rejection of realism and, more broadly, that talk of transcendental or ultimate ontology is meaningless.

The Epistemology of Ontology[7]

To my mind there has always been a fundamental tension in Quine's work between his commitment to a kind of scientific realism, on the one hand, and his frequent employment of proxy functions and the rejection of transcendental metaphysics, on the other. Quine has defended his brand of scientific realism and naturalism (1992a). He has expanded his defense (1993, 1996), utilizing observation sentences in their holophrastic guise (Quine 1993). He has argued (1993) that the latter bear "significantly on the epistemology of ontology" and that they provide for the commensurability of theories. I argue that they fail in all these tasks. Further, Quine's long-standing commitment to a kind of scientific realism, on the one hand, and his frequent employment of proxy functions and the rejection of transcendental metaphysics, on the other, constitute an untenable position. A consistent Quinean must abandon scientific realism and ontology. I also argue that, insofar scientific realism is a robust ontological thesis, we all must abandon it, along with traditional ontological talk, for it is meaningless.

Quine (1993) tells us that when observation sentences are taken *piecemeal*, i.e., when component terms of observation sentences in their referential capacity is at issue, they are theory laden, but when they are treated *holophrastically*, linked as a whole to the current stimulations and independent of any possible subject matter, there is no theory dependence. It is in the latter capacity that observation sentences are pure, pristine, "the child's port of entry into cognitive language" (1993, p. 109). And later, "Holophrastically . . . the observation sentences are anchored to sensory neural intake *irrespective of their theoretical subject matter*" (1993, p. 110, emphasis added). Quine praises the virtues of observation sentences in their holophrastic capacity. He maintains (1993, pp. 110–112) that they serve as common reference points for incommensurable theories and advance the epistemology of ontology, among other things.

Subsequent to his 1993 paper, Quine has given up the claim that holophrastic observation sentences are independent of theory. In a response to a series of earlier versions of the present chapter, Quine came to agree that the relevant holophrastic observation sentences are theory dependent.[8] Nevertheless, Quine appears reluctant to accept the fact that this concession undermines the alleged virtues of observation sentences just mentioned. In what follows, I detail the theory dependence of an important class of holophrastic observation sentences to show how this forces a rejection of Quine's realism.

In *Word and Object*, Quine spoke of units geared as wholes to stimulations,[9] which I will call *one-word observation sentences*. Holophrastic observation sentences correspond somewhat to these, but only somewhat; as we shall see, holophrastic observation sentences go beyond one-word observation sentences in a crucial way. The piecemeal treatment corresponds to what Quine earlier described as the move to accepting certain analytical hypotheses, which enabled parsing sentences into terms and dividing the reference of the latter (*WO*, pp. 68–73, 90–95).

A small part of the problem with Quine's discussion of observation sentences in his 1992 and 1993 papers is that he conflates two distinct dimensions pertinent to talk of observation. The dimensions are (1) degrees of observationality and (2) whether a sentence is taken piecemeal or holophrastically. Quine "rescinds" degrees of observationality in his 1996 paper, but the way he does so does not obviate the problems spelled out in this chapter. Quine tends to identify sentences treated holophrastically with those of high degree of observationality.

A more serious problem is the conflation of the earlier idea of a one-word observation sentence with the idea of a sentence taken holophrastically. This problem and its consequences will be examined in detail in what follows.

To see how holophrastic observation sentences go beyond one-word observation sentences, I will divide the observation sentences Quine considers in his 1993 paper into a series of levels, epistemic considerations determining the level of a given observation sentence. It is the fact that some holophrastic observation sentences go beyond one-word observation sentences that disables them from performing the epistemic tasks Quine assigns them. (The one-word observation sentences are also inadequate to the tasks but for different reasons.)

Note first that Quine's point in praising observation sentences is to provide an intermediate ground between classical epistemology, with its foundational view, and the anti-foundational views found in the works of N. R.

Hanson, Paul Feyerabend, and Thomas Kuhn. Quine suggests that the move from phenomenalism to physicalism was due at least in part to the realization of the inadequacy of the idea that there is a phenomenalistic conceptual scheme somehow given from which we can posit the physical world (1993, p. 107). For Rudolf Carnap, Otto Neurath, and Moritz Schlick, the issue became one of specifying what sentences to count as "protocol sentences." Quine asserts that "subsequent physicalists were impatient with even this" and that "they shelved the whole notion of epistemological starting point, and therewith the last remnant of epistemology" (ibid., p. 108). He thinks they gave up too easily, for he tells us that what to count as protocol "becomes clear, if one is both single-mindedly physicalistic and single-mindedly epistemological" (ibid.).[10]

Quine seeks to reactivate, in modified form, the notion of "epistemological starting point," a notion abandoned by earlier physicalists. He thinks his notion of holophrastic observation sentence can play that role and can provide an intermediate ground between the classical epistemological foundationalists and the contemporary anti-foundationalists. He states that "the protocol sentences [which he subsequently calls "observation sentences"] should be the sentences most closely linked causally to this neural intake [the impact of molecules and light rays on our sensory receptors] . . . , sentences like 'It's cold', 'It's raining', 'That's milk.'" (1993, p. 108) He recognizes an obvious objection to such sentences serving as an epistemic foundation is that *they already assume knowledge of the external world* and so they are of dubious evidential support for such knowledge. He seems think he meets this objection. I argue that he is unsuccessful.[11] To this end, I now introduce the first of the levels of my epistemic classification of Quine's observation sentences, the purest form of observation sentences, level 1: "Observation sentences—as I call them—can be conditioned outright to distinctive ranges of sensory intake, or as physicalists let us say neural intake. The child can be conditioned simply to assert or assent to the sentence under some distinctive stimulation. . . ." (Quine 1993, p. 108) Such sentences avoid the objection just noted. However, if observation sentences are to be powerful enough to do the *epistemological* work that Quine has in store for them, he recognizes he must broaden the class further. In addition to observation sentences such as these, there are others, which I place in level 2: "We learn some of them from other ones by analogy, recombining their parts. We learn to form compounds of simple ones, using grammatical particles." (ibid.) Not even this is enough. Observation sentences must encompass even more. Level 3: "As adults, we learn many more *through the mediation of sophisticated theory*. Thus, take the sentence 'There is some copper in the solution'. We understand it by construction from its separate words, but it becomes an observation sentence for a chemist who has learned to spot the presence of copper by a glance at the solution." (ibid., emphasis added)

Why does Quine count sentences of what I have called levels 2 and 3 as observational? We are told that "what qualifies sentences of both sorts as observational, for a given individual, is just his readiness to assent outright on the strength of appropriate neural intake, irrespective of what he may have been engaged in at the time" (ibid.). This criterion for a sentence's being observational is relative to an individual and, to borrow an expression from Feyerabend, is "quickly decidable." Whether a sentence is taken as a unit or parsed with terms taken in their referential capacity is irrelevant to its being quickly decidable for a given individual (or for an entire community). Such matters, however, are *not* irrelevant with respect to the question whether knowledge of the world is already assumed. Quine must contend with the latter if he is to establish the epistemic virtues of his observation sentences.

In my classification, for a sentence to be of level 1 it must be treated as a one-word observation sentence. Such sentences, of course, are not intrinsically one-word observation sentences—no string of marks or sounds is intrinsically a one-word sentence; a sentence may be parsed and treated non-holophrastically, *but when so treated it is no longer a level-1 observation sentence*. Thus, while both level 1 and level 3 may be quickly decidable and holophrastically considered, these features are not sufficient to qualify a sentence as a one-word observation sentence. Level-1 sentences are restricted to the latter.

There are many ways one might partition Quine's class of observation sentences, depending on one's purposes. My levels 1 and 3 are chosen so as to highlight an epistemological point, one that exposes the inadequacy of the class of Quine's observation sentences to do the epistemic work he sets for them. In particular, level 1 is restricted to one-word observation sentences to isolate those and only those that do not presuppose knowledge of the world. Sentences that I place in level 3, however, are those that Quine tells us are learned "through the mediation of sophisticated theory." As such, they do not qualify as one-word observation sentences, even though they can be treated holophrastically and are (often) quickly decidable. Being treated holophrastically and being a one-word observation sentence are, for these reasons, importantly different.

Quine's inclusion of level-3 sentences among the observational is necessary, however, if one is to have any hope of obtaining a basis for knowledge of the world—level-1 sentences by themselves are too weak. But including the level-3 sentences undermines his attempt to meet the obvious and fundamental objection he recognized to the initial protocol sentences offered by early positivists: Knowledge of the world is assumed. For example, a chemist's response "There is copper in it" to seeing a green precipitate is clearly dependent on the chemist's (assumed) knowledge of the world.[12] This is in no way contravened by the fact that on various occasions it is holophrastically treated or quickly decidable. Level-1 sentences avoided this objection by remaining unparsed; they are by stipulation one-word observation sentences, each geared to some distinctive stimulation. No knowledge of the world is presupposed; such sentences are not parsed into terms that refer. In saying this I am not holding that it is impossible to parse them. No one claims that any utterance or string of marks intrinsically constitutes a one-word observation sentence. The point is simply that, given the epistemic partitioning of the class of observation sentences that I have offered, when a level-1 sentence is parsed it ceases to be a level-1 sentence—by that very fact. Parsing unavoidably introduces assumptions about the world, whether they are widely held assumptions (such as that there are medium sized physical objects) or assumptions of some specialized group (say, chemists).

The idea of a one-word observation sentence, a level-1 sentence, is importantly different from both the idea of a holophrastic observation sentence and the idea of one that is quickly decidable; Quine uses the latter feature to warrant sentences of level 3 as observation sentences. But some sentences of level 3 are subject to the initial objection; they assume knowledge of the external world. That level-3 sentences may be quickly decidable or holophrastically treated in no way circumvents this objection. The *epistemic differences* between level-1 and level-3 sentences are obscured when Quine emphasizes their common holophrastic treatment. Important consequences of these points for ontology will be specified below, but first more must be said about Quine's treatment of observation sentences.

For Quine, observation sentences are "Janus-faced." Facing inward, the subjective side, "the neural intake is keyed to the sentence as a monolithic

whole, no matter whether the sentence was first acquired by simple ostension [level 1] or by excursion through theory in the manner of the chemistry example [level 3]" (1993, p. 109). The last clause of this quote makes it
evident that Quine allows for the holophrastic treatment of level-3 sentences. This is certainly permissible. Whether doing so avoids the charge of
assuming knowledge of the world is a separate question. I am arguing that
it does not. We can see the same point in another light if we examine the
other face of these two-faced sentences.

Quine tells us that observation sentences also face outward to their subject matter. This is their objective side, and thus construed "the sentence
figures not holophrastically, but piecemeal word for word" (1993, p. 109).
Furthermore, *observation sentences in their outward guise* are also, he tells us,
"the vehicle of evidence for objective science, intersubjectively attested"
(1993, p. 109). Since it is in their outward guise that observation sentences
are the "vehicle of evidence for objective science," it is at level 3, not at level
1, that sentences play this role. But level-3 sentences presuppose knowledge
of the world, unlike level-1 sentences. The epistemic neutrality of level-1
sentences is not transferred to level-3 sentences, even when the latter are
recognized as Janus-faced, treated holophrastically, or quickly decidable.

The degree of objectivity of the outward-facing observation sentences is
further compromised by what Quine says is "the further requirement for
our definition, [viz.,] that assent to the sentence and dissent from it must
command agreement of all competent witnesses" (1993, p. 109). Who will
count as competent? *Those who have the requisite knowledge.* In the chemistry
example, it is obviously those who have knowledge of the relevant chemi-
cal theory and, therefore, the knowledge to interpret the green precipitate
under the appropriate conditions as indicative of the presence of copper.
Never mind that the sentence "There is copper in it" is quickly asserted or
assented to and is keyed to the stimulation as a monolithic whole and thus
treated holophrastically. An observer would not, and could not, quickly
assert or assent to such a sentence, holophrastically or otherwise, without
the appropriate knowledge—knowledge that goes far beyond the immediate stimulations.

Importantly, it is also clear that observers lacking the requisite knowledge
would not even count as competent observers. (Of course, lacking that
knowledge, an individual might well quickly respond "It turned green," but
that is another matter entirely.) To provide an "epistemic starting point"

not subject to anti-foundational criticisms, as Quine wishes, the candidate observation sentences must not assume knowledge of the world. That the sentences can be treated holophrastically does not circumvent this problem; holophrastic treatment of these *presupposes* prior parsing, for they are learned through the mediation of theory; thus, there are attendant assumptions about the world. Their subsequent holophrastic treatment does not eliminate the assumptions required that such treatment presupposes.

In response to an earlier (July 1993) version of the present chapter, Quine reports that he attaches "importance to a distinction quite close to that between your [i.e., my] levels 1–2 and level 3; namely, in my case [i.e., Quine's], between sentences that are observational relative to the whole community of normal speakers of the language and ones that are observational only relative to a trained subclass. I shall call them the primitive and the professional observation sentences." He further notes that, though both "serve as checkpoints in the experimental method," persistent questioning force the scientist ultimately to rely on the primitive observation sentences. But whether the primitive observation sentences coincide with those of levels 1 and 2 turns on how broadly based the community of normal speakers of the language is taken to be. If, for example, a sentence pertaining to medium-size physical objects is observational for the whole community of normal speakers of the language, then, while such a sentence would count as primitive, it would not count as a sentence of levels 1 and 2. It could not be included since it assumes knowledge of the external world; the references of its terms are divided. So, in general, our distinctions are not co-extensive.

As I stated earlier, the point of the classification of level 1 is that for sentences in this level *no knowledge of the world is assumed*. The point was *not* that there was general agreement on them. Nor was the point that no sentence of level 1 could be parsed—they all *can* be (as I have repeatedly stated). However, when this occurs, assumptions about the world are made, and the sentence so treated no longer counts as a level-1 sentence. I will call sentences of levels 1 and 2 *proto-observation sentences*. It is clear that Quine's notion of a *primitive observation sentence* is, in general, more inclusive in its extension. It is also worth repeating that widespread agreement on the primitive observation sentences does not imply that they lack any built-in assumptions about the world. Because the primitive and the proto-observation sentences differ in these ways, truly persistent questioning of a scientist would force him to rely on the latter, not the former.

If the above is correct, Quine's argument against incommensurability is called into question. He says that observation sentences are "shared reference points for the two theories," and that "comparing the responses of the two theories to these shared checkpoints, then, should afford traces of commensurability insofar as the two theories are under empirical control at all" (1993, p. 111). He notes that this requires that the observation sentence in question be learned holophrastically. But how such sentences are learned or used is not as critical as what they presuppose in the relevant epistemic context. Whether such sentences are learned or used holophrastically is a red herring. The real point is that for sentences to serve as epistemically neutral checkpoints they must do their epistemic work *as one-word observation sentences*, with no assumptions about the external world. Only proto-observation sentences will do, if any will.

The sentences *themselves* of levels 1 and 3 may be treated holophrastically or not, but a fundamental difference between the levels is that level-3 sentences epistemically presuppose a great deal of theoretical knowledge *from the very beginning*, regardless of whether they are holophrastically treated or not. Therefore, level-3 or primitive observation sentences (insofar as the latter go beyond proto-observation sentences) are disqualified as impartial arbitrators between theories. The foundational epistemic burden, if it is to be borne at all, must go to the one-word observation sentences, *as* one-word observation sentences. Proto-observation sentences may serve to force revision or rejection of a theory inconsistent with them—they may serve as "negative check points" (Quine 1993, p. 111). What they cannot do is discriminate between empirically equivalent theories, for being consistent with the same range of proto-observation sentences is a necessary condition for the theories' being empirically equivalent.[13] Observation sentences that can discriminate are not epistemically basic; they are parsed, and they presuppose some ontology. Thus, the intermediate epistemological ground between foundationalism and anti-foundationalism, which Quine sought to secure with his Janus-faced observation or protocol sentences, has slipped away.[14]

Holophrastic Observation Sentences and Realism

Let us now examine these results in relation to Quine's realism. His long-standing position is that science tells us what there is and what what there is does. (See my discussion of (3) below.) We have just seen how, according to Quine, holophrastic observation sentences play an important evidential role in science; furthermore, Quine states that the holophrastic role of observation sentences "bears significantly on the epistemology of ontology" (1993, p. 112). Having said that, he continues, as he has so often done in the past, in a rather odd fashion:

(*) Their association with neural intakes, being holophrastic, is *unaffected by any reassigning of objects to the terms involved*. But also the logical relations of implication that connect scientific theory with observation categoricals [i.e., pairs of observation sentences combined into generalizations such as 'When it snows, it's cold'] are unaffected by one-to-one reinterpretation of terms; all that matters to logical structure is identity and difference. We conclude that *the sensory evidence for science is indifferent to what things science says there are*, so long as identity and diversity among them is preserved. . . . *So far as evidence goes, objects figure only as neutral nodes in the logical structure of our total theory of the world*. (1993, p.112, emphasis added)

Certainly holophrastic observation sentences play an important evidential role in science, and science tells us *how* the world is. Given (*), however, it seems impossible for science to tell us *what* there is, i.e., for it to have any bearing on ontology. If the objects assigned to the terms and predicates of a theory are mapped one-to-one to different objects to preserve the logical structure of identity and difference, then we have two interpreted theories, though only one formal theory. Clearly, the formal theory could not be a candidate for telling us what is in the world. By hypothesis, the interpreted theories have different ontologies, though the evidential support for them is the same. Which is the correct ontology? If, as Quine says, "so far as evidence goes, objects figure only as neutral nodes in the logical structure of our total theory of the world" (1993, p. 112), the evidence cannot adjudicate here. This, however, is what they must do if their holophrastic role is to bear significantly on the epistemology of ontology, as Quine claims (ibid.). Though in other kinds of cases the holophrastic observation sentences may serve as "negative checkpoints," as indicated above, this has no direct bearing on the positive question as to what there is.

If one is to eschew transcendental metaphysics, as Quine counsels, there is a tension between the claims of scientific realism, endorsed by Quine, and the claim that the bodies assigned to terms of a theory can be swapped without affecting the observation sentences which support the theory. This is a deep tension, one that I think is traceable back through many of Quine's writings. Here I will cite only a recent occurrence of this conflict.

Drawing on his earlier writings, Quine challenges the objectivity of our idea of an object:

(1)   The very notion of an object at all, concrete or abstract, is a human contribution, a feature of our inherited apparatus for organizing the amorphous welter of neural input. (1992a, p. 6)

In the same article, Quine makes the point he made in (*), one which he has made repeatedly over the years by appealing to proxy functions, viz.,

(2)   . . . if we transform the range of objects of our science in any one-to-one fashion, by reinterpreting our terms and predicates as applying to new objects instead of the old ones, the entire evidential support of our science will remain undisturbed. . . . Once we have an ontology, we change it with impunity. (8)

Quine recognizes that this view "may seem abruptly at odds with realism, let alone naturalism" (9), but he explicitly rejects this conclusion and makes the following assertion:

(3)   The world is as natural science says it is, insofar as natural science is right. . . . (9)

I have no quarrel with (1) and (2). Jointly, they provide support for abandoning transcendental metaphysics or, simply, ontology. My point is that all this also compels the rejection of any robust reading of (3).

I just noted that Quine recognizes no conflict between his acceptance of (2) and (3), despite the appearance to the contrary. How does he purport to resolve the conflict? He says this:

Naturalism itself is what saves the situation. Naturalism looks only to natural science, however fallible, for an account of what there is and what there is does. (9)

Science itself, Quine tells us, must use man-made concepts and man-made language, "but we can ask no better. The very notion of object, or of one and many, is indeed as parochially human as the parts of speech; to ask what reality is *really* like, however, apart from human categories, is self-stultifying. . . . [This is essentially the point of (1); however, he continues:] But early positivists were wrong if and when they concluded that the world is not really composed of atoms or whatever. The world is as natural science says it is, insofar as it is right. . . . (9)

If the only reservations to holding the claim that natural science tells us what there is were (a) that science is fallible, (b) that our concepts and language are man-made, and (c) that the very idea of an object is also man-made, I would have little trouble embracing (3), so long as (3) was understood in light of (a)–(c). But it is (2), the point of proxy functions, together with the inadequacy of observation sentences to the epistemic tasks that Quine wishes to put them which ultimately undermines (3), as argued above.[15]

There is an anemic reading of (3) that dissipates all conflict between it and (1) and (2). On this reading, "the world is as natural science says it is" amounts to no more than the claim that a certain set of *words* is used in science, rather than some other possible set. This is a reading consistent with Quine's attempt to rescue reference from nonsense in "Ontological Relativity" (pp. 26–68). In chapter 8, I argued at length that these attempts by Quine to rescue reference from nonsense fail. I will not rehearse the details of those arguments here, except to show that Quine's considerations already challenged fare no better in preserving his brand of realism.

Having argued that inscrutability of reference applies to oneself, Quine seeks to avoid the apparent nonsense this makes of reference by "picturing us at home in our language, with all its predicates and auxiliary devices. . . . In these terms we can say in so many words that this is a formula and that a number, this is a rabbit and that a rabbit part. *In just those words*. This network of terms and predicates and auxiliary devices is, in relativity jargon, our frame of reference, or coordinate system. . . . Reference *is* nonsense except relative to a coordinate system. In this principle lies the resolution of our quandary." (ibid.) He goes on to tell us that it is meaningless to ask what our terms *really* refer to: "It is meaningless to ask this absolutely; we can meaningfully ask it only relative to some background language." (1969, p. 48) Relativizing to a background language, Quine also notes, gets us into regress of background languages, and this is cut off in practice by "acquiescing in our mother tongue and *taking its words at face value*" (1969, p. 49, emphasis added). Thus, "taking words at face value" not only is critical to rescuing reference from nonsense and terminating the regress of background languages; it also plays a central role in explaining the sense in which the world is as natural science says it is.[16]

Though reading (3) along these lines eliminates the inconsistency with (1) and (2), it is a most anemic reading. A customary understanding of scientific realism is that the presumed referents of the terms of a successful scientific theory *actually* exist. Granted, 'realism', even 'scientific realism', has a number of distinct construals, but when the term is used in the same context as 'ontology', then the suggestion, if not the implication, is that the realism at issue is that the terms of our best scientific theories refer to real objects in the world. In contrast, the anemic reading suggested presents an ontology in name alone. It is reminiscent of Carnap's rejection of ontological questions in the external sense.

Carnap argued early on that when there is no empirical difference between linguistic frameworks (theories), questions as to what there is really, apart from such theories, what he dubbed "external questions," are meaningless (1956, pp. 205–221).[17] Thus Carnap downgraded ontology all the way. He contrasted external questions with internal questions, which were meaningful existence questions that could be answered within the linguistic framework (theory). However, Carnap did not hold that one would then be a realist with respect to the accepted theory except, perhaps, in the most diluted form that his analysis of internal existence claims allowed. The external questions are within the realm of transcendental metaphysics, which both Quine and Carnap reject. The anemic reading of (3) is in accord with restricting questions of existence to internal ones. If this is all scientific realism comes to, however, it is misleading to call it *realism*. Better to abandon all talk of ontology, downgrade it all the way, as Carnap did.

There is, however, an important difference between Carnap and Quine on this score. To my knowledge, Carnap never made much, if anything, of what Quine calls "proxy functions." Nor did he take into account the points, as expressed in (2) above, which may be made by appeal to such functions. It was the fact that Carnap did not utilize proxy functions and did not make realist claims that enabled him to speak of internal existence claims without the difficulties that Quine gets into. Carnap rejected external existence questions outright and deliberately trivialized the internal ones. Quine rejects external existence questions too,[18] for he eschews transcendental metaphysics. But it is Quine's use of proxy functions that significantly contributes to the tension between (2) and (3). This is most evident when (3) is asserted in the context of ontological issues, as Quine typically does.

My point is that either (3) must be given an ontologically anemic reading to be consistent with (1) and (2), or (3) must be rejected. But in either case, ontology is downgraded all the way. If Quine restricts himself to the anemic reading, then he does downgrade ontology all the way and, in that case, it would be better to drop all misleading talk of *scientific realism*. Quine, however, appears as reluctant to abandon talk of scientific realism as he is to go all the way.

An Apparent Way Out Fails

Support for a more robust realism may be sought along different lines, but within Quine's naturalism. I pursue this path only to show its inadequacy. Consider some things Quine maintains in "Epistemology Naturalized" and in "Natural Kinds."[19] One might reason that we may rely on the man-made categories of natural science to tell us what there is because these categories naturally evolve from our inquiring interactions with nature; there is no higher court of appeal. Furthermore, the "similarity determined by scientific hypothesis and posits and constructs" is based on and a development from a more "immediate, subjective, animal sense of similarity" (Quine 1969, p. 134). The latter is a result of an innate standard of similarity, an "innate qualitative spacing of stimulations." So, there would seem to be a more or less direct line from what stimulates us and the categories of science.

The innate-similarity standard might, in some sense, provide a basis for saying what there is (shades of classical empiricism, no doubt), but only in a weak sense, and one which is ultimately inadequate to the task. The innate qualitative spacing of stimulations could at best account for one-word observation sentences. When it comes to dividing the reference of terms, and thus to imposing categories of objects, such innate quality spaces are not fine-grained enough to do the job. So, innate quality spaces can offer no grounds for some particular kind of objectual reference. Thus, it offers no grounds for holding that science tells us what there is.

This attempt to rescue Quine's realism meets more obstacles. Similarity classes determined by science are even more remote from the stimulations at our surface than are those resulting from our "animal sense of similarity." Any hopes one might have had along this line are further dashed when it is realized that as science develops the similarity standard itself becomes superfluous, for the relevant phenomena are defined in virtue of their underlying structures, as Quine himself points out. Now add to this the crucial fact, expressed in (2), that the categories of our science pertaining to that underlying structure can be mapped one-to-one to different categories, while still being true to the observation sentences. Once again, it appears that (3) must be jettisoned along with the rest of the metaphysical flotsam.

The Dilemma for Holophrastic Observation Sentences

The problems that I argued plagued Quine's conception of observation sentences reflect problems that epistemologists of the first half of the twentieth century faced. Quine, of course, is acutely aware of those problems. He notes that one important aspect of Carnap's Aufbau project was of a piece with that of "the old phenomenalist epistemology [which] inspired a project of rational reconstruction, the derivation of natural knowledge from sense data" (1993, p. 111). A problem, perhaps the central problem, for any such reconstruction was that if the sense data were taken narrowly enough so that they could serve as a safe neutral epistemic foundation, one could not get back to physical objects, let alone our natural knowledge of them. Alternatively, if the basis was taken more broadly to overcome such meager and debilitating beginnings, then the basis itself was called into question; it no longer was epistemically neutral. Among the others involved with versions of these problems were Bertrand Russell, C. I. Lewis, and A. J. Ayer.

Quine's attempt to find an intermediate ground between classical epistemic foundationalism and recent anti-foundationalism confronts a similar dilemma. His observation sentences must be pared all the way back to level 1 to be epistemically neutral. Thus, they are not referential, and they are silent on what there is. They themselves are not sufficient to secure objects in the world, and theories with different ontologies are consistent with them. Piecemeal, they are no longer neutral adjudicators between radically different but empirically equivalent theories with different ontologies. So in neither orientation can they resolve incommensurability or ontological issues.

Closely related to the classical project of constructing physical objects out of sense data was the equally Herculean task of establishing the meaningfulness of theoretical statements or terms on the basis of observation statements or terms. Again, Carnap led the way and many followed. These massive efforts also failed.[20] This series of failures—essentially the downfall of Logical Positivism—resulted in the abandonment of the observational/theoretical distinction, the rejection of the idea that anything was "given" in sense perception that could serve as a foundation for knowledge or meaning, and the realization that the very idea of a pure observation was illusory. What emerged was the belief that there is a continuum from the more observational to the more theoretical, theory intruding in varying degrees throughout. Moreover, it was realized that the orientation of the line of the continuum itself varies depending on which theories are accepted. These outcomes were among the things that led to the various anti-foundationalist positions.

It is anti-foundationalist programs based on such results that Quine hopes to derail in resurrecting the observation sentence. He is, of course, keenly aware of the problems the epistemologists of the first half of the twentieth century faced. He mentions, in particular, the fact that observation sentences are theory laden as a serious source of misgiving as to their being up to the foundational tasks the early epistemologists of this century wished to put them. It is precisely this problem that he hopes to circumvent by treating observation sentences holophrastically, for he locates the problem in taking observation sentences piecemeal.

Holophrastic Conditioning versus Holophrastic Treatment

In his 1996 paper, Quine contrasts his earlier views on observation sentences (in *Word and Object*) with his more recent views, such as those put forth in his 1993 paper. In the earlier work, he recognized degrees of observationality as a function of how much theory or collateral information intruded. This is in accord with the development of the Positivists' view of the matter, recently sketched herein. But Quine maintains the following:

. . . in later writings I held observationality as absolute, based on immediacy of assent, and then I accommodated the intrusion of theory by contrasting the *holophrastic* conditioning of the observation sentence to neural intake with the *analytic* relations of the component words to the rest of language. The sentence figures holophrastically both in the infant's first acquisition of it and in the scientist's immediate assent to it when testing a theory. (1996, p. 162)

I have argued that the immediacy of assent is not sufficient to secure "observationality as absolute." There are crucial epistemic differences between an infant's first acquisition of a sentence and a scientist's immediate assent to a sentence. Here we have immediate assent marking the holophrastic use for the scientist. But if I have argued correctly, this holophrastic use, the immediate assent to a level-3 sentence by a scientist, does not warrant giving it the same epistemic status held by level-1 sentences, the one-word observation sentences. Though the immediate assent may mark that the sentence figures holophrastically, it does not circumvent in itself the analytic relations between the words of the sentence. The immediate assent to a sentence is not sufficient to deny the intrusion of theory, but it is just this lack of intrusion that is the hallmark of level-1 sentences.

There is also an important difference between the acquisition of a sentence by holophrastic *conditioning* and the holophrastic *treatment* of a sentence (already acquired) marked by immediate assent. Typically, level-3 sentences are not holophrastically *conditioned*, though we will see below that they may be. In contrast, level-1 sentences can only be acquired by holophrastic conditioning. A child's first acquisition of certain sentences (e.g., 'Mama') fits here whereas a level-3 sentence such as "There is copper in it" is typically learned through the analytic relations of its word parts, i.e., through the intrusion of theory. Even so, it may be immediately assented to by a scientist given the appropriate stimulation and so, in Quine's sense, figure holophrastically. This, however, does not make it holophrastically conditioned, nor does it eliminate the intrusion of theory. On the other hand, one who has learned the appropriate theory can holophrastically condition *someone else*, someone ignorant of all the relevant theory, to immediately assent to or assert the sentence under appropriate stimulation. For an ignorant individual thus trained (and it matters not how many are thus trained), "There is copper in it" is a one-word observation sentence, but it is not a one-word observation sentence for the trainer or for the community in the know, even when they immediately assent under appropriate stimulation. The point is that the trainer, in order to carry out such holophrastic conditioning, must already have mastered the relevant theory.[21]

So, I repeat, while one can immediately assent to or have holophrastic uses of level-3 sentences, this cannot serve as a basis for treating "observationality as absolute," contrary to Quine's claim (1996, p. 162) These characteristics of sentences do not in themselves have any bearing on their roles as adjudicators for competing theories or for establishing scientific realism. Immediacy of assent or holophrastic treatment is not to the epistemic point. Only one-word observation sentences (of level 1) could play these epistemic roles—the sentences that are holophrastically conditioned without the benefit of someone's knowledge of the relevant theory. (Of course, although these are candidates, they are not adequate to these tasks.)

Recapitulation of Some of the Main Points
Observation sentences taken piecemeal are certainly theory laden, and I have argued against Quine's claim that treating them holophrastically can

transform them into objective arbiters between competing theories and ontologies. Just why this result obtains turns on the fact, argued above, that level-3 observation sentences are theory laden even when they are immediately assented to or taken holophrastically: Holophrastic or not, level-3 sentences assume knowledge of the external world. It is only the level-1 observation sentences, the one-word observation sentences, that are not theory laden. Level-1 sentences—as a condition of membership—can only be treated holophrastically. Once parsed, they no longer count as level-1 sentences, and the initial objection of assuming knowledge of the world applies. In contrast, level-3 sentences may or may not be treated holophrastically, but their holophrastic treatment, unlike that of the one-word observation sentences, is no sign of their epistemic neutrality. As was argued earlier, the ability of those in the know of the relevant theory to immediately assert or assent to the sentence under appropriate stimulatory conditions is necessarily based on their possession of the relevant theory. Therefore, holophrastic observation sentences of level 3 are theory laden in spite of any immediate assent to them and cannot objectively resolve epistemic foundational issues or ontological questions, except negatively, as indicated earlier.

Two Dimensions of Observation Sentences

I now turn to the two distinct dimensions pertinent to Quine's treatment of observation sentences mentioned at the onset; I will show how their conflation contributes to Quine's belief that observation sentences can do more than I have argued they can. For convenience, I take the continuum of observationality, degrees of observationality, to be one with that of the most observational to the most theoretical.[22] The elements of this continuum, however, do not match the holophrastic/non-holophrastic distinction. As we have seen, whether a sentence is holophrastic or not has to do with its circumstances of use, how much one knows, and how one was trained, and not with its epistemic status. Thus, it is not only sentences of highest observationality that can be treated holophrastically; we may so treat sentences right up the scale, well into the heavily theoretical area, if not all the way to the end. Where do the one-word observation sentences fit on this continuum? They are off the scale to the left of the most observational. The epistemic gap between the one-word observation and the most observational sentences on the scale is due to the fact that the latter may still be taken piecemeal and remain highly observational. One-word observation sentences, *as* one-word observation sentences, are never taken piecemeal. Doing so changes their status.[23]

Quine (1996, p. 162) tells us that he retains "the absolute notion of an observation sentence as simply an occasion sentence that commands the subject's immediate assent, however fallible and revisable. Fallibility is then accommodated in a separate dimension, *theoreticity*, which invests observation sentences in varying degrees." He comes to this conclusion after reflecting "further on the bipolarity of the holophrastic and analytic perspectives, as against the gradualism [degrees] of observationality in *Word and Object*" (ibid.).[24] Whether one speaks of degrees of observationality or of immediate assent, the following question remains: Can the observation sentences do the epistemic and ontological work they are assigned?

The subject's immediate assent does not pick out a distinct dimension for "the absolute notion of observation sentence," as Quine claims (1996, p. 162). Fallibility is not the fault that I press here, rather it is the work that the proxy functions do. Immediate assent is too broad a net for the absolute notion of an observation sentence, as it encompasses both level-1 and level-3 sentences; theory intrudes significantly in level 3 but not in level 1. If I am right, it is only the one-word observation sentences that are absolute in Quine's sense, and they are not adequate for the epistemic and ontological tasks that have been under discussion.

What is important for present purposes is that the high degree of observationality of sentences such as "There is a cup on the desk" does not in any way depend on their being treated holophrastically: They remain highly observational sentences even when treated piecemeal. The latter does not detract from their high degree of observationality. At the other end of the scale, the fact that many, perhaps all, sentences of level 3 can be treated holophrastically does not transform them into epistemically neutral sentences. Conflating the idea of observation with the idea of a sentence's being treated holophrastically obscures this last point. Only one-word observation sentences escape theory dependence, and thus only they are epistemically neutral. These sentences, however, are not sufficiently robust to have any positive epistemic bearing on ontology. Nor, as argued earlier, are they able to positively resolve conflicts between competing global theories.

By focusing on the possibility of treating sentences holophrastically and invoking the idea of quick decidability or immediate assent, levels 1 and 3 are conflated. For some purposes such common grouping of these levels may be desirable. I have tried to show that for positively resolving issues around the competition of theories and the epistemology of ontology such common grouping is intolerable. Ontology must be downgraded all the way.

Epilogue

So there it is. Consciousness and subjectivity are broader than the phenomenal. They permeate both the intentional and the phenomenal, and they are crucial to linguistic meaning. I hope by now you are convinced that the concept of minimal content provides a unified foundation for both a theory of mind and a theory of language, whereas the orthodox, strictly third-person methodologies applied to these areas have inherent flaws. My theory corrects those flaws by recognizing the primacy of the subjective in a way that does not immerse us in a "touchy-feely" morass of subjectivity. Why has this plain, immediately accessible datum of minimal content been overlooked? The answer is simple. Minimal content is invisible to the orthodox methodology.

What accounts for this debilitating methodological restriction and the consequent failure to recognize the primacy of the subjective? I speculate that there have been two main sources, both rooted in a careless extension of the orthodox methodology from domains in which it properly applies (those in which there is no privileged first-person perspective, such as the study of cells) to domains in which we do have a first-person perspective: consciousness. First, the Positivists articulated a detailed view of scientific method that they forcefully and persuasively advanced. For them the only way to objectivity was through a strictly third-person methodology. Their view of scientific method had tremendous influence in philosophy and beyond. Arguably, it had a tremendous impact on psychology as psychologists endeavored to be scientific by positivists' lights. The result was Behaviorism. Part of the significance of this was that virtually any talk of consciousness became suspect, as it was not amenable to study by the favored methodology. As the inadequacies of Positivism and Behaviorism became evident, they were eventually abandoned; nevertheless, the firm grip of the idea that a strictly third-person methodology is necessary for any objective study remained. It continues today, usually under the guise of "naturalism." Second, Wittgenstein's private language argument reinforced this aversion to the subjective and the use of first-person methodologies. I have argued that the limited privacy of language found in my theory is not pernicious. Indeed, it is essential.

The primacy of the subjective in the study of mind and language is unavoidable. Importantly, it can be accommodated without compromising the objectivity of our results or burdening us with dubious ontological commitments.

Notes

Chapter 1

1. In chapter 3, I will explain why these theories separated these two aspects.

2. Without suggesting that they all hold exactly the same view, I will note that those advancing the idea of phenomenal intentionality include David Chalmers (1996), Terence Horgan and John Tienson (2002), David Pitt (2004), Charles Siewert (1998), and Galen Strawson (1994).

3. I will argue in chapter 3 that this strategy rests on a mistake.

4. This feature depends only on the fact that we sometimes know without inference part of what our thoughts are about in some sense. It is not that we know all of it in this way. It is not that we always non-inferentially know part of it. It is not even that we need explicitly entertain what that content is. To make my case, it is enough if the agent has been, or could become non-inferentially aware of part of the content of his thought in some sense; I do not need that he is always so aware. These restrictions will become clearer below. Nor is the claim that we have special access to our own minimal contents to be confused with maintaining a private language or anything like that. The special access is not due to the "privacy" of minimal contents; others are not precluded from having knowledge of another's minimal contents. It is just that their knowledge of mine must be inferential, whereas my access to my minimal contents can be non-inferential. Compare the discussion of one's forming an image or drawing a diagram and other cases discussed below. (Also compare Davidson 1984, 1987.) How and why we can have objective knowledge of another's minimal contents is discussed in chapter 3 and the last section of chapter 5. The extent to which my theory commits me to the privacy of language (hardly at all, and without pernicious consequences) is discussed in chapter 8.

5. David Armstrong (1963) argues against the claim that *all* introspective reports are incorrigible. Even if his argument for this is sound, it does not refute my claim that *some* introspective knowledge is incorrigible. Moreover; Armstrong's arguments assume that incorrigibility claims must be confined to a "perceptual instant," but

none of my arguments for infallible knowledge of minimal content are contingent upon this assumption. Similarly, R. Nisbett, T. Wilson, and A. Gopnik (see McGeer 1996, p. 496) argue that psychology rejects the presumption that first-person reports should be accepted, barring good reason to override; they appeal to various evidence in support of this. Here too the kinds of error they find are irrelevant to my concept of minimal content, defined below, and our infallible knowledge of it.

6.   Shoemaker (1990) attempts to provide for a limited privileged access that is neither infallible nor transparent but which is available to the externalist. Donald Davidson (1987, 1984) argues for the importance of first-person authority and points out that some ignore or dismiss it, while others fail to see the seriousness of the problem it poses for externalist views of mental content. He notes (1988) that, while Burge (1988) acknowledges first-person authority, he does not adequately show how such authority can be reconciled with his view. (See my discussion of Burge in chapter 7, where I show this failure undermines his famous thought experiment.) Though the problem is serious, Davidson argues that first-person authority can be reconciled with an externalist view of content. In chapter 2, I argue that Heil's (1988) attempt to advance a Burgean view of first-person authority or privileged access is unsuccessful in reconciling first-person authority with externalism. I also argue there that any externalist account must fail, including those like Davidson's, which appeal to the natural history of the agent. The asymmetry of access that I argue for is like that upon which Davidson's bases first-person authority in that it turns on the agent's non-inferential knowledge of the content of one's thought, but the content that I argue for which is governed by first-person authority is much narrower than Davidson's. For him, there is special access to our occurrent beliefs, desires, and other propositional attitudes as these are ordinarily understood (1987, p. 447), what is often referred to as wide content. The content that I argue we each have privileged access to is a "narrow content." We shall also see that it is not to be identified with what is normally referred to as narrow content.

7.   Although the example is Heil's (1988, p. 248), I exploit it in ways he would not endorse.

8.   There is a reading of the word 'subject' in the locution 'subject of the intentional state' that is legitimate but is not my intended usage, viz., as the individual who has the intentional state. My usage concerns a restricted part of the intentional content of the intentional state. For example, if I believe that Mary is beautiful, Mary is the "subject" of my intentional state, not me, not the thinker. Scare quotes are used here because it is this use of 'subject' that I argue has two readings: as minimal content and objective content.

9.   Holding this does not entail that whenever I am in a state that can be said to have minimal content that I must also be explicitly aware of that minimal content on that occasion. (See my warning in an earlier note.) The awareness spoken of here is simply the non-inferential knowledge of what is represented by the minimal con-

tent, not the noticing of some special feature of the state or its minimal content. And that's a good thing, for it would seriously count against my view. As to why this is so, see, e.g., Kripke 1982, especially the latter part of part 2.

10.   Though Searle's most extended account is to be found in his 1983 book *Intentionality*, a particularly clear discussion of the differences between intrinsic intentionality and derivative or metaphorical intentionality appears in Searle 1984. It is worth noting that acceptance of Searle's framework for an analysis of intentionality, as he presents it in the early chapters of *Intentionality*, does not commit one to the acceptance of the causal account of intentionality he gives in the final chapter. Too often arguments against the latter are mistakenly thought to argue against the former.

11.   This move, a shift of types, has parallels with Frege's identification of the referent of an expression in oblique contexts with its customary sense. On my view this shift to a new type of referent is not required. More on the relations between Frege's view and mine later.

12.   A recent view that is motivated by this line and differs with Searle on this point is advanced in Crane 2001. In a paper under review, I argue that Crane fails in this and that Searle's view is superior.

13.   This way of putting it is borrowed from Searle (1983, p. 6). The decomposition of this schema discussed immediately below goes beyond Searle.

14.   One might think that the same rational that leads to distinguishing m and o would force recognition of a similar distinction for Φ. This is not so. The point in making the distinction between minimal content and the objective content is that there are compelling grounds for analyzing the 'subject of the agent's thought' in two different ways. For purposes of analysis, there are no similar grounds for holding that Φ should be similarly analyzed. When the agent is "off" regarding the attribution of Φ, it typically is a result of a deficiency in her *understanding* of Φ. The difference between understanding and awareness will be introduced in the next section and will be discussed further elsewhere in the book.

15.   It is interesting, if not surprising, to garner some support for something like my distinction between minimal content and content objective content from a paper by Willard Van Orman Quine (who undoubtedly would have protested the use of his distinction in support of mine). Quine's 1994 paper also brings out an additional advantage of treating intentional states as I do, viz., a basis is provided for accommodating the treatment of sentences expressing intentional states, decomposed as (i) and (ii) , within the syntax of predicate logic. Quine is not alone when he asserts that "no theory is fully clear to me unless I can see how this syntax [that of predicate logic] would accommodate it" (ibid., p. 144). My proposal may be viewed as a suggestion that also enhances the clarity of our understanding of intentional states in this regard, one that is different from Quine's quotation-based solution that he offers

in the mentioned paper. Quine attaches great importance to the subject's point of view in the treatment of propositional attitudes in the paper cited. For example, he notes that the failure of substitutivity in belief contexts stems from the fact that "the subordinate clause of the construction is uttered *from the subject's point of view* . . . and . . . the subject . . . didn't know the things were identical" (ibid., p. 145, emphasis added). My formulation differs from Quine's, but it is the same kind of distinction at play. On my theory, the subordinate clause expresses the thinker's minimal content and requires an instantiation of $\Psi(\Phi(m))$ rather than of $\Psi(\Phi(o))$, and the thinker may not know that m and o signal the same thing. Additionally, Quine notes that the "quantification $\exists x$ (Ralph believes that x is a spy) raises an ontological problem of the value of 'x'" (146). I agree, as I do with his diagnosis that "the difficulty, again, is just discrepancy between the real world, to which the outlying '$\exists x$' relates, and the empathized world—Ralph's—in which the recurrence of 'x' is trapped" (146). I suggest a different resolution of this problem raised by Quine: Employ expressions for the objective content when the real world is at issue, and employ expressions for Ralph's minimal content when it is a question pertaining to the "empathized world," for in the empathized world, the subject of the thought as conceived by the agent is at issue, not the subject that an objective observer would ascribe.

16.   Talk of "actual objects in the world" is to be understood here, and throughout, as simply those objects upon which there is inter-subjective agreement within a given community. No deep ontological claim is being made. The reasons for this and some of the consequences will be apparent in chapters 8 and 9.

17.   Someone may object at this point and insist it is not clear that the content is numbers in one case and sets in the other, since it is not even clear what numbers and sets are apart from the role they play in a theory. (See Benacerraf 1965 or Resnik 1981.) If the question were "What does the objective content indicate?" I would be inclined to agree, but that is not the question. There is a clear sense in which what A and B *conceive* their respective objects to be is distinct. No matter how that difference eventually gets cashed out, and no matter what the ultimate nature of numbers and sets—as minimal contents they are distinct. Taking the position that numbers and sets are nothing apart from the relations that they enter into (and, thus, insofar as they enter into the same relations, they are the same contents) is to give a theoretical account of the *ontological* status of numbers and sets, one that might even be right. Similarly, if one holds that numbers are ultimately certain kinds of sets, that there are no numbers. Thus, such considerations bear on our *understanding* of numbers and sets; they do nothing to explain the appearance of awareness of minimal contents, and different ones at that.

18.   I suggest that minimal content can be useful in an analysis of *fictional objects*. Normally, an agent attempts to have her minimal contents signal the same subjects as do the objective contents of her thoughts; whenever she learns they do not match, she aligns her minimal content so that it does. Things are otherwise with fic-

tional objects. A fictional object is simply the subject of a thought as conceived by the thinker, her minimal content represents an object that she *knows* does not exist, she knows the objective content of her thought is empty, so *efforts toward realignment are deliberately excluded.*

19.   To challenge this one would have to give an extremely strong holistic account of meaning. One that would have as a consequence that the content of 'number' is different for our theorists A and C because of their differing ability to manipulate the symbols. If we were to accept this, we might wonder whether two individuals ever could have the same content, inasmuch as it is doubtful that two individuals would ever actually have identical symbol-manipulating abilities. (The unrealistic assumption that A and B have identical symbol-manipulating abilities was made strictly for the sake of argument.) The results here further support the importance of distinguishing explicating and individuating. (Compare below.) See my discussion of Burge in chapter 7, where I discuss the conditions for saying two individuals have the same concept even when there is not an exact match between their conceptions.

20.   The 'pre' in 'pre-axiomatic' should not be understood temporally. Perhaps a more accurate prefix would be 'extra.' It may well be questionable whether the objects are grasped apart from *any* theory or background language whatsoever (see chapters 8 and 9), though I do not think that Rota et al. are making such a strong, unrestricted claim.

21.   They state: "Since there is no one group, but groups come in incredible variety, such a pre-axiomatic grasp of the notion of group cannot be attributed to familiarity with a single group. One could argue that such an understanding is derived from familiarity with several groups and their 'common' properties, but this would amount to begging the question, since familiarity with more than one group presupposes an unstated understanding of the concept of group that permits one to recognize several instances as being instances of the same general mathematical structure." (Rota et al. 1989, pp. 381–382)

22.   In chapter 7, I will show how this point can be used to undermine Burge's famous thought experiment, which he offered on behalf of anti-individualism. How it bears on meaning will be discussed in chapter 8

23.   The uniqueness of minimal content in this regard will also provide for the resolutions of some problems regarding representation (chapter 5) and some others I will raise for Quine regarding his theses of Indeterminacy of Translation and the inscrutability of reference (chapter 8).

24.   This regress problem is not always noticed by those who employ a strictly third-person methodology. David Armstrong is an exception. I discuss the problem in the context of giving an analysis of representation and Armstrong's (unsuccessful) attempt to block the regress with his appeal to a claim that simple concepts are

intrinsic representations in chapter 5 and show how the fundamental intentional state solves this problem.

25. I am grateful to John Bickle, whose persistent (stubborn) resistance several years ago to my claim that consciousness is required for representation contributed to my development of the idea of a fundamental intentional state.

26. This kind of indeterminacy problem is discussed in detail in chapter 8 in conjunction with Quine's thesis of the Indeterminacy of Translation. The latter thesis undergoes a radical modification in light of the results herein.

27. To the extent that appropriate symbol manipulation is a component of understanding, to that extent it would be correct to speak of such programs as instantiating understanding of number theory, and some instantiating a better understanding than others. Whether the sense in which such programs "understand" is anything more than metaphorical is another question, because whether appropriate symbol manipulation is merely a measure of understanding, is actually partly constitutive of or sufficient for it has yet to be determined. On the distinction between metaphorical and intrinsic intentionality, see Searle 1984. Here we are also touching on problems raised by Searle in his famous Chinese Room, discussed below.

28. Compare Dretske's statement that "unless the symbols being manipulated mean something *to the system manipulating them*, their meaning, whatever it is, is irrelevant to evaluating what the system is doing when it manipulates them" (1985, pp. 27–28). I agree with Dretske that the important and relevant case is that in which the symbols mean something for the system processing them, though I disagree with him on what this amounts to or whether his approach can adequately deal with it. In addition, I prefer to put the point in terms of the system's privileged access to its minimal content. For Dretske's more recent development, see his 1997 book *Naturalizing the Mind*. The exact nature of my disagreement with him is made explicit in chapter 5, where I argue that his account of representation is seriously defective.

29. The capacity to have access to one's minimal content is closely related to an item having any content *for* the system, human or otherwise, that deploys the item. The idea of a symbol having content for a thinker is developed further in chapters 5, 7, and 8.

30. In contrast to the minimal content, the objective content is objective and, in this respect, it is more like a Fregean sense, or rather a truncated Fregean sense, for unlike the latter, it only indicates objects, not states of affairs. Of all the concepts that I have employed, however, it is probably that of representative content, understood with an objective content rather than with minimal content, which is closest to a Fregean sense.

31. One might argue that my distinction between minimal content and objective content aligns somewhat with Descartes' distinction between objective (sometimes

translated as 'presentational') reality and formal reality, respectively. See *Meditation 3*. Confusingly, what is translated as 'objective reality' denotes, in Descartes, something more like what we would now think of as subjective.

32.   The latter alternative holds, since minimal content is just a component of the representative content, R, on one of its decompositions, $\Phi(m)$.

33.   This is developed in Searle 1980. The case somewhat simplified is essentially as follows: An English-speaking person is locked in a room and provided with a large ordered store of sequences of Chinese characters together with a set of elaborate syntactic transformation rules. The latter are formulated in English, but operate on strings of Chinese characters. The individual in the room does not understand Chinese. However, given new strings of Chinese characters from someone outside the room, he is able to apply the transformation rules to the received strings so as to produce new strings that he then passes out of the room. A Chinese-speaking person on the outside is passing meaningful Chinese sentences to the man in the room, and the latter, unknown to himself, is returning meaningful and appropriate Chinese responses.

34.   Compare my discussion of Galileo in chapter 4. Galileo also attempts to explain certain common-sense appearances that seem to conflict with his view.

35.   It is reported that Johnson uttered "Thus, I refute Berkeley" while kicking a stone.

Chapter 2

1.   Armstrong (1968, 1980), Lycan (1987, 1992), and Rosenthal (1986, 1990, 1991) advocate higher-order theories of consciousness. Armstrong and Lycan build their theory on a perceptual model, a higher-order theory of perception (HOP). Rosenthal's theory of consciousness appeals to higher-order thoughts (HOT). My argument stands against either version.

2.   All page references here are to Heil 1988. Heil strongly relates self-awareness to second-order intentionality, though he only takes the latter to be one way of being self-aware. Of the latter he says: "I shall use the expression 'self-awareness' in what is perhaps a non-standard way. I am concerned here only with the capacity to 'introspect' on mental states and goings-on, not anything more elaborate. I shall not address, for instance, the ability sometimes ascribed to human beings to focus inwardly on an ego, self, or other mental substrate." (242, n. 7) This use of the locution is widespread. However, I think it is misleading to call it '*self*-awareness', since it seems only to involve awareness of (one's own) mental contents, and so awareness of "*self*" indirectly, at best. I will continue to call it 'awareness of content' or 'privileged access to content'; I use the latter when the emphasis is on the asymmetry between first-person and third-person access. I continue to refrain from using 'self-awareness'. A further word on 'content': Heil does not hold that one is always

aware of the content of one's thought, nor do I. Nor does either of us hold that one is ever aware of all the content of' one's thought. It is enough that one is sometimes aware of at least part of the content of one's occurrent thought. I made these qualifications in chapter 1. For Heil's qualifications, see pp. 238–242 of his 1988 paper.

3. This formulation is Heil's. It is taken from some correspondence we had before the publication of my 1990 paper, which criticized his 1988 paper. I am grateful to him for the correspondence.

4. Still, they may not be all that different. In all three cases, one might identify the external condition determining the content to be some neural state, and one distinct from that determining the corresponding thought having that content. We may have some reason to think that there is such a state. However, this much 'externalism' would not seem enough to satisfy most externalists; the key to externalism is to incorporate features of the environment external to the subject's body. In any case, establishing this would still leave one open to the charge that it is the sign rather than the content that is determined.

5. I discuss this point regarding the particularity of a representation in considerable detail in chapter 5.

6. See note 4 for a candidate, though for the reason given in that note it is not helpful to externalism.

7. Regrettably, it is not uncommon for philosophers to equivocate on "intentional content" and "intentional object." This leads to conundrums when what the intentional state is about does not exist (and others), conundrums that can be avoided by resolutely distinguishing the two, as both Searle and I, in my extension of Searle's theory, do.

8. My discussion of Van Gulick's views on understanding, semantic transparency, and just how phenomenal consciousness figures in an account of them is restricted to his 1989 paper. (I first criticized these views in my 1996 paper.) He has, however, presented these views in several other essays (e.g., Van Gulick 1988, 1993).

9. As we will see, it is not clear that Van Gulick thinks phenomenal representations are separate from *human* understanding, though it is clear that he thinks they are separate from *understanding*. The distinction between understanding and human understanding reflects the functionalist position that whatever has the right functional relations, human or non-human, will exhibit understanding. Van Gulick entertains the possibility that phenomenal representations may be contingently tied with human understanding, though not a feature of understanding, generally.

10. The issues concerning particular contents are of fundamental importance. They have been discussed some already, but a thorough discussion occurs in chapter 5.

11.   I am grateful to Henry Jacoby for raising the objection to a much earlier version of this argument.

12.   Not that no one is trying. The deepest and most sustained effort of which I am aware is that of Zenon Pylyshyn (1986). Pylyshyn plausibly maintains that a program meant to model some psychological phenomena should be *strongly equivalent* to it and takes important steps toward providing an account of strong equivalence. In brief: "In my view, two programs can be thought of as strongly equivalent or as different realizations of the same algorithm or the same cognitive process if they can be represented by the same program in some theoretically specified virtual machine. . . . The formal structure of the virtual machine—or what I call its *functional architecture*—[is] the sort of functional resources the . . . [system] makes available. . . . Specifying the functional architecture of a system is like providing a manual that defines some particular programming language. Indeed, defining a programming language is equivalent to specifying the functional architecture of a virtual machine. Thus the way I address the issue of the appropriate level of comparison between a model and a cognitive process—or the notion of strong equivalence of processes—is to provide a specification of the functional architecture of a "cognitive virtual machine." (91–92) The determination of the *functional architecture* of the brain is crucial to Pylyshyn's overall project, as he himself stresses; indeed, he argues that "*any* notion of correspondence stronger than weak equivalence [i.e., simply input/output equivalence] must presuppose an underlying functional architecture, or at least some aspects of such an architecture" (92). One of the reasons for this is that any program that models cognitive processes must not merely *emulate* the way the brain does it (see, e.g., 98–99), but the basic operations used in the program must be the same as the basic operations used by the brain, if they are to be strongly equivalent. If it is to be a model of cognitive activity, it must *execute* the program in the same way as does the brain. However, "since . . . there is no well-developed theory of algorithmic equivalence in computer science, these ideas must be developed without benefit of an existing body of analysis" (115). This is not as damaging to the project as one might at first suspect since, as he stated earlier, "the relevance of formal criteria [for algorithmic equivalence] to cognitive-science goals is marginal (we are not concerned with the task of comparing two *programs* but with comparing a program and a set of empirical phenomena); the pursuit of strong equivalence in computer science is of interest because it reveals underlying conceptual issues" (90). Of course, one such issue is the importance of the distinction between the functional architecture and the cognitive process so as to assess strong equivalence claims (260). Pylyshyn's work is probing, rich, and important. He is defining a research program for the study of cognitive processes. One of the *goals* of the program is to develop a notion of strong equivalence. Since the models are not merely to emulate the cognitive processes, he further requires an empirically based criterion for determination of the functional architecture of a system. He plausibly argues for two independent empirical criteria for zeroing in on the functional architecture of a system, what he calls *complexity equivalence* and *cognitive impenetrability*, but he also notes that "there

is no way to guarantee in advance that both criteria pick out the *same* level of functional architecture" (114). It is worth repeating that the relatively precise and rigorous field of computer science lacks a "well-developed theory of algorithmic equivalence" (115). Pylyshyn certainly does not think that the criterion for strong equivalence in cognitive science is an accomplished task. So, in spite of the importance and fruitfulness of Pylyshyn's work, it cannot be offered in rebuttal to my claim that there is (now) no principled criterion of functional equivalence. Should his or a similar project come to successful fruition, my argument that depends on the fact that there is no principled, non-ad-hoc criterion of functional equivalence, would need restructuring. Until then, my argument cannot be rebutted by appeal to a possible assumed principled criterion of functional equivalence. The *possibility* of such a criterion certainly cannot by used to claim that two *specified* systems, such as A and B, are not functionally equivalent, for it would beg the question.

13. See Carnap 1966, pp. 131–133.

14. Some of these same points against the functionalist can be made, somewhat surprisingly, by appealing to Quine's theses of the Indeterminacy of Translation and the inscrutability of reference. I discuss these in chapter 8.

15. Further possibilities that result by reversing the causal or logical relations or holding that the content and verbal disposition are independent need not detain us here, since they block, rather than advance, my objector's case.

16. In chapter 4 I do this for brain states and mental states, states that appear to be of radically different kinds. Hence, I avoid a similar criticism of my theory when I later claim that having a conscious state is the same as having a certain sort of brain state.

17. This appearance is of a different type than the one discussed in the previous paragraph. On what is involved in explaining this sort of appearance, see the last section of chapter 1.

18. There is an important issue here that often is overlooked. When it is said that a causal interaction between the system or creature and its environment is required to determine or individuate content the proponent of such a claim is usually silent as *to whom* the content is thus determined. I examine this crucial point in detail in chapter 5. See also what I have said about "determining the content" earlier in this chapter and about individuating content in chapter 1.

19. It should be obvious, though, that what I am here characterizing as minimal content is distinct from what is often considered to be narrow content, i.e., conceptual or inferential role. While one might reject minimal content, one certainly cannot identify it with this sense of narrow content. For the classic discussions of narrow and wide content and of Twin Earth, see Putnam 1975. An important issue surrounding the concept of narrow content is whether it is required for psychological explanation. Brian Loar (1988) and Ned Block (1986) argue, contrary to Burge,

that narrow content is required for psychological explanation and that the main challenge to this view is to "find a non-arbitrary way of constraining the relevant connection, so that each psychological state can turn out to process a determinate narrow content, and to explain how this constrains its truth conditions" (Loar 1988, p. 8). Here "relevant connection" refers to a concept's inferential connections to other concepts, in accordance with both Loar's and Block's concept of narrow content, which is distinctly different from my narrow concept of minimal content. If my arguments are thus far correct, inferential connections, functional role semantics, lacks the resources to determine a *particular* content. I develop different arguments to the same conclusion in chapters 5 and 8, and I also show there how my concept of minimal content is a determinate narrow content that does constrain it truth conditions. I am not here directly concerned with the question as to whether the notion of wide content is itself adequate for a science of psychology, or whether one also needs some notion of narrow content for such purposes. There are many issues pertaining to this important question that I do not address in this book; nevertheless, I do think psychological explanation does require some concept of narrow content, and I think minimal content can make a contribution here. In particular, it is uncontroversial that to understand an individual's behavior we must know how *she conceives* things, since she deliberates about things and acts (seeks or avoids) in accordance with how she thinks things are. Knowing how she conceives things is especially important when there is divergence from how things are objectively. Behavior that is aberrant to objective observers is sometimes driven by just such divergences.

20.   In saying this I am not holding that the identity of concepts, or the meaning of terms are ultimately determined by the individual. See my discussion of Burge in chapters 1 and 7 and my discussion of Quine in chapter 8.

21.   The differences between explicating and understanding content, on the one hand, and individuating content, on the other, were discussed in chapter 1.

22.   See Burge's discussion of his arthritis example (1979) and Davidson's criticism of it (1987). Although I have many points of agreement with Davidson on these and related issues, the fact that he ultimately bases his points on the causal histories of the agents undermines, in my opinion, his conclusions, or so I argue below. For my discussion of Burge, see chapter 7.

23.   Some years ago John Heil raised this objection in response to a paper of mine that presented this argument.

24.   Of course, an individual's knowledge may change in time so that his minimal contents represent the different entities in his new environment (say, when he is transported to Twin Earth and learns of XYZ) or correctly represent what was always in his environment (say, when the phlogiston chemist learns the oxygen theory of combustion). But when this happens, surely his thoughts are different than they were. Although his minimal content and objective content would now signal the

same entity, this has no bearing on their earlier divergence. So, when the phlogiston chemist gets converted to the oxygen theory of combustion, his new thoughts about burning objects will have both his minimal content and objective content signaling the same entity, without altering the fact that in his earlier thoughts, while causally interacting with an environment similar to the current one, his minimal content and objective content diverged in what they signaled.

25. Davidson (1987, p. 455) makes a similar point. Whether I am right about these views on content sharing an ancestry with classical empiricism is quite immaterial to my other points.

26. Typically, of course, we take the objects our minimal contents represent to actually exist. This is an additional belief, however, one which is independent of our having minimal contents, of our conceiving our thoughts to be about this or that. That our thoughts have minimal content is in no way dependent on this further belief about them. Moreover, when we discover that there is no corresponding objective content or that it is different from our minimal content, we abandon that minimal content and attempt to align our new minimal content with the objective content. However, we do not always do this: when I contemplate a fictional object, I know that the minimal content and the objective content do not match—that is the point of a fictional object.

27. In chapter 8, however, I will argue that sentence or word meaning ultimately depends upon minimal content.

28. Compare my discussion of Johnson's purported refutation of Berkeley in the last section of chapter 1.

Chapter 3

1. Horgan and Tienson (2002, p. 520) have dubbed this division *separatism*.

2. Searle is an important exception here. His Chinese Room thought experiment is very explicit in its focus on *understanding*. Unfortunately this has not stopped others from recasting Searle's case in terms of *phenomenal* consciousness. See, for example, Van Gulick 1989 and my discussions of that paper in Georgalis 1996 and below.

3. See chapter 2, where I argue that functionalism has not even succeeded here and reasons are provided as to why it cannot do so.

4. Certainly phenomenal states are or can be conscious, but it is not as clear that every conscious state is or can be phenomenal. I have argued (chapter 1) that there are non-phenomenal conscious states, pace Tyler Burge (see below), and that this is of importance in showing the role consciousness—without phenomenality—plays in intentionality.

5. See, for examples, Dretske 1995; Harmon 1990; Lycan 1996; McDowell 1994.

6.   Of course, insofar as the representationist is willing to countenance my analysis of intentionality, then that would be quite another matter. I would then be open to her position, though I think certain other problems do arise for this view, even if this augmented view of intentionality were adopted. I do not go into these other problems here.

7.   Among other reasons for this is that Block defines the latter functionally. See chapter 2 for why a functional analysis will not work here.

8.   Mentality is in fact a broader concept than (genuine) intentionality, contrary to the suggestion in the quoted passage. A generalized pain or anxiety is mental without being intentional. (Searle and others have made this point.) This aside, the first premise, even as stated by Van Gulick in his reformulation of Searle's argument, does not assert that semantic transparency is *required* for the broader notion of mentality; however, as stated, it does for the narrower notion of genuine intentionality. In any case, Van Gulick's recasting of Searle's concept of genuine or intrinsic intentionality in terms of semantic transparency is not a reformulation that he would accept.

9.   Though I did not employ the locution 'semantic transparency', I did speak of symbol manipulation, and one of my points was that there could be a great deal of sophisticated (and rapid) symbol manipulation without there being any phenomenal content.

10.   Without suggesting that they all hold exactly the same view, I note that those advancing the idea of phenomenal intentionality include David Chalmers (1996), Terence Horgan and John Tienson (2002), David Pitt (forthcoming), Charles Siewert (1998), and Galen Strawson (1994). Horgan and Tienson, for example, explain it as follows: "*Phenomenal Intentionality*: There is a kind of intentionality, pervasive in human mental life that is constitutively determined by phenomenology alone." (520) They offer what the they claim is a sharper formulation: "There is a kind of intentional content, pervasive in human mental life, such that any two possible phenomenal duplicates have exactly similar intentional states vis-à-vis such content," where "two creatures . . . [are] *phenomenal duplicates* just in case each creature's total experience, throughout its existence, is phenomenally exactly similar to the other's" (524).

11.   We saw above that Davies and Humphries do identify Nagel's "the something it is like" with phenomenal consciousness.

12.   Sometimes the WIL is extended in a third, more general, way: what it is like for a conscious being on any given occasion to be in some occurrent intentional state—a combination of attitude with content. Authors who agree that there is a WIL experience to intentional states may still differ as to which of these different extensions (attitude, content, or combination thereof) of the restricted sense is operative. I will largely ignore such differences in my discussion, as no new issues are raised by these variants.

13.   The qualification to *this sort* of WIL is made because, as I will argue below, there is a sense of WIL that is operative, one that is connected to our first-person awareness of our minimal contents but which in no way implicates the phenomenal.

14.   To say this is not to deny the existence of what Galen Strawson has called "understanding-experience" involved in intentional states, of which he says: "To talk of understanding-experience, then, is not to commit oneself to the implausible view that there is some single qualitative type of experience that anyone who has understanding-experience must have. It is not to commit oneself to the view that particular qualitative experiences invariably go with understanding particular sentences." (1994, p. 7) Indeed, he seems to be in explicit agreement with my denial that the WIL of intentional states delivers any uniform phenomenal feature, as he further states: " . . . we need to allow that a particular case of understanding-experience can involve a specific cognitive experiential content while overcoming the tendency of the words 'specific experiential content' to make us think only of distinctions like those found in sensory experience." (13) I am in complete agreement with him on this, as I am with his claim that it is of the utmost importance to recognize the fact of understanding-experience. But Strawson thinks that the concept is "elusive" and there is little hope of doing anything theoretical (11) because it "evades description" (12). I disagree with his expressed pessimism. While I have not previously used the locution 'understanding-experience' I believe that what I have said in chapters 1, 5, and 8 does address in considerable theoretical detail the issues raised by the concept of understanding-experience.

15.   I thank Natika Newton for raising this objection, which prompted the response that follows.

16.   Saying this is not to deny that some phenomenal aspect or another is associated with an occurrent intentional state, but when it is, it is only contingently associated with it—unlike minimal content. I argued above for the contingency claim.

17.   The idea that there is something non-phenomenal that is *for* an agent is also crucial to my theory of representation, see chapter 5.

18.   Commenting on the expression "what it is like," Nagel says that "it does not mean 'what (in our experience) it *resembles*,' but rather 'how it is for the subject himself'" (1980, n. 6). I think the use of 'how' here is appropriate and informative for phenomenal states, but in keeping with my suggestion in the text, I suggest '*what* it is for the subject himself' when propositional attitudes are at issue. Though clearly in saying the latter, I am not appealing to what it *resembles*.

19.   I recall David Chalmers commenting, in a conversation, that he uses these terms interchangeably, and even adding 'consciousness' to the list. (I extend my apologies to him if this report is inaccurate.) Horgan and Tienson begin their 2002 essay by asking "What is the relationship between phenomenology and intentionality?" and proceed to discuss "phenomenal aspects." They also state the theses of

"The Intentionality of Phenomenology" and "The Phenomenology of Intentionality" in terms of "phenomenal character"; moreover, they then proceed to explain "Phenomenal Intentionality" using the word 'phenomenology'.

20.   For it turns on applying what I called the unrestricted sense of the WIL locution, and this fails to deliver a type-identifying uniform phenomenal feature of intentional states. The case is no better for the application of the unrestricted sense of WIL to uncover a "phenomenological" aspect of intentionality, and for the same reasons. More on this below.

21.   Compare note 14 above, in which Strawson is quoted admonishing us to accept a different reading of the locution 'specific experiential content' than that found in sensory experience.

22.   One might object that since others can think the same *thoughts*, they are in fact objective. This objection, if it were sustainable, would prove too much. For the case is no different for phenomenal experiences: When I am cognizant of a green apple on the table because of my perceptual experience, the subjectivity of this experience is not threatened because others can be cognizant of the same thing. Here as in the case, say, of the thought that two is a prime number, others may think the same thoughts as I do without undermining the fact that there are subjective aspects to both of these thoughts. I have assumed here that my minimal contents and objective contents signal the same things. When this is not so, the subjectivity of my thoughts, whether perceptual or non-perceptual, is even more evident. In both the phenomenal and the non-phenomenal cases, *what* is experienced, in one sense, may be objective without affecting the subjectivity of the experience itself.

23.   I will extend the analysis I have given of intentionality to that of phenomenality in chapter 6: both require minimal content and objective content.

24.   Of course, Mary's task is far more difficult than this suggests. Often we use a color term in the absence of any thing of the color of which we are speaking—e.g., "My car is green" in the absence of any green thing. This exacerbates Mary's problem, though it does not preclude obtaining correlations of brain states with actual color perceptions.

25.   This claim may draw support from no less authority than Ernest Nagel. In his classic book, before closing his discussion of state descriptions, he states: "One final point of considerable importance should be noted. A definition of the 'state of a system' suitable for a given empirical subject matter, cannot be supplied *in advance* of an adequate "causal" theory for that subject matter." (1961, p. 292) Nagel further explains that he understands a theory to be causal "if it relates time-rate of changes in some set of magnitudes with other magnitudes." The set of magnitudes is the set of relevant variables that I referred to above.

26.   See my chapter 5. There I also examine a related issue concerning the conditions for saying that a non-human has representational states.

27.   There is some reason to think that Nagel would agree with my earlier claim that we can have objective knowledge of subjective states and the claims made in this paragraph and those regarding Sally, for consider the following passage: "There is a sense in which phenomenological facts are perfectly objective: one person can know or say of another what the quality of the other's experience is. They are subjective, however, in the sense that even this objective ascription of experience is possible only for someone sufficiently similar to the object of ascription to be able to adopt his point of view—to understand the ascription in the first person as well as in the third. . . ." (Nagel 1980, p. 163)

28.   Though, of course, the objectivity just referred to is not one restricted to an exclusively third-person methodology. In the last section of chapter 5, I will argue that a third-person methodology that also incorporates a first-person perspective for the study of subjectivity can be objective in a legitimate sense of that word; moreover, failure to incorporate the first-person perspective in the philosophical or psychological study of the mind leads, contrary to what might be expected, to anthropomorphism. I also introduce a methodological principle, methodological chauvinism that encapsulates the points made herein.

29.   I am very grateful to Bill Lycan for his generosity with his time, both in conversation and correspondence. Though I am sure he does not agree with what I say in this section, he was able to eliminate some of my misunderstandings of his view. No doubt some remain. (My comments on Lycan are based on the manuscript of Lycan 2003.)

30.   Compare my discussion of nomic and non-nomic properties in chapter 5 in connection with the role consciousness plays in representation.

31.   Lycan explains that this premise, coupled with the hypothesis that Mary knows every physical fact about color experience prior to exiting her color deprived room would entail that materialism or physicalism is false, since Mary appears to learn a new fact upon release. Hence, he is concerned to deny that Mary learns a new fact. In contrast, while I argue that Mary does learn a new fact on release from the room, I draw no ontological conclusions from this, nor do I think that any follow. As to my aversion to ontological matters, see chapter 9.

32.   I would like to thank Michael Veber for his resistance in conversation to my claim that that Mary learns a new fact, as the presentation below is better than it would have been otherwise.

33.   Mary can consider what it would be like because she is not deprived of all subjective experience, though she has of yet had no color perceptions

34.   It is actually an empirical matter whether Mary would straight-away see colors when released. Nevertheless, as the thought experiment is usually discussed, including by those who advocate an ability hypothesis, it is taken for granted that Mary does see colors straight-away upon release.

35.   David Chalmers (1996, p. 118) also holds this. He argues in a similar vein that some explanation of how this comes about is required, if we are to seriously treat the proposal. But I also show in the next chapter wherein I disagree with his arguments and the conclusions he draws, and I propose my own solution to the problem.

36.   There is also an additional problem for feature (2) of the Inner Sense Theory being of any help in resolving the "how possibly" question, if what I argue regarding representation (chapter 5) is correct. For then what Lycan calls 'representation' in feature (2) falls short of being representation.

37.   I hasten to add that Lycan (1996, 1999) has addressed the "how possibly" question; indeed, he thinks that he has answered it. I do not examine his interesting proposals here. I think he fails primarily for two general reasons. Higher-order perception theories are no better off than higher-order thought theories with regard to accounting for our first-person, first-level awareness of content, and I have already argued against the latter theories. Secondly, the very idea of representation already requires the concept of consciousness, as I argue in chapter 5; so, it cannot be used to explain consciousness

38.   Nagel may or may not agree. As to why he may agree, see the quotation in note 27.

39.   In addition to what I have already said in support of this, I explain that this does not make the investigation unscientific in the last section of chapter 5.

40.   It is well known that David Chalmers (1996) is credited with coining the former expression and Joe Levine (1983) the latter.

Chapter 4

1.   It is important to stress this ordinary observational sense of the term. David Chalmers objects to this analogy, used in a distant ancestor of this chapter. His objection is based on a different interpretation of 'liquidity'. His objection goes as follows: " . . . the water case is not a useful analogy for you, because in that case it's clear that what needs to be explained is structure and function—we explain the liquidity, transparency, etc. and it's obvious that those are the sort of structural/functional matters that are wide-open to physical explanation." (email, December 13, 1998) For it to be "obvious" that these properties are open to a structural/functional explanation, one must presume, at the least, that these properties are understood in a physio-chemical way, rather than in the way I recommend here, a way that corresponds to our ordinary observation of liquids. I will have more to say about the role of structure and function in these matters below. In chapter 6 I will argue that these two interpretations of 'liquidity' reflect a wide spread and systematic ambiguity in all sensory terms.

2.   Similarly for solidity of ice, where much stronger intermolecular bonds keep the individual molecules in fixed position relative to one another; in the case of water vapor, the individual molecules have such high energy that they are unable to form intermolecular bonds and move freely with respect to one another.

3.   Searle utilizes the molecule/liquidity case in an attempt to show that there are no metaphysical obstacles to an account of our intentional states as causal features of our brains. He claims our mental states are genuine biological phenomena that are both "caused by and realized in the brain," a claim that, among other things, seems to introduce a notion of mental-physical causation. He has been widely criticized on this point. My aim here is neither to review these criticisms nor to defend Searle on this matter. Instead, I will examine one of the ways that Searle does try to dispel the air of mystery, as my case is similar though different from his. The difference is important. Searle illustrates the idea of something being caused by and realized in something else by making an analogy to how liquidity is both caused by a kind of molecular motion and realized in that molecular behavior. In fact he cites the analogy as one that is parallel to Leibniz's famous case of imagining a giant machine that could think, feel and perceive. One so large, that we can walk into it as though it were a mill. On so doing we would find parts that interact with one another, but never find perception or any other mental state. Similarly, in the case of a liquid we would not find the liquidity at the level of the molecules. Searle holds that "in both cases we would be looking at the system at the wrong level. The liquidity of water is not to be found at the level of the individual molecule, nor are the visual perception and the thirst to be found at the level of the individual neuron or synapse. If one knew the principles on which the system of H_2O molecules worked, one could infer that it was in a liquid state by observing the movement of the molecules, but similarly if one knew the principles on which the brain worked one could infer that it was in a state of thirst or having a visual experience." (1993, p. 268) What we have in all these cases is that certain macro-phenomena are caused by and realized in certain micro-phenomena. This may be so, but the trouble is that right now it is difficult to see how the firing of neurons or the passing of chemicals across synapses *could* give rise to intentionality in a way analogous to how we can see how non-liquid molecules and certain sorts of bonds between them *can* give rise to liquidity. (Searle has mentioned to me that Thomas Nagel has raised a similar objection to his use of the analogy.) I offer a resolution to this objection below and also have something to say about mental/physical causation.

4.   The concept *comprehensible to us* is itself a subjective concept. This may be another reason why so many physicalists imbued with a strictly third-person methodology eschew or downplay the problem of the explanatory gap. See below.

5.   I raised these points in criticism of John Heil's treatment of supervenience in my 1995 review of his 1992 book. Apparently, he now agrees, for in the conclusion of his 1998 paper he states: "I have argued that the concept of supervenience as standardly formulated provides little in the way of ontological illumination. . . .

Supervenience is not explanatory. . . . Supervenience claims hold, when they do, because the world is a particular way. *What we need to be clear about is what that way is*. Different cases yield different results." (emphasis added) The emphasized passage is what I argued for in my 1995 review and held that without it supervenience claims are uninformative and useless.

6.   As to the competition between options 1 and 2, one is reminded of one of Kuhn's claims. Often when a given scientific paradigm, say, the current network of neurophysiological practices and theories, is under pressure because of its apparent inability to solve some outstanding problem, those strongly committed to it are willing to postpone work on this problem. They are confident that new techniques, methods, or information, all compatible with the existing paradigm, will be obtained that eventually will allow solution of the problem. They would endorse option 1. Others see the problem as refuting the existing paradigm, preparing the way for a new paradigm. They would endorse option 2. (Despite what I just said, I do not hold that there is a single paradigm in contemporary neuroscience).

7.   Colin McGinn (1989) has argued for such a pessimistic conclusion.

8.   These physicalism/anti-physicalism "wars" ultimately presuppose an untenable view of substance, or so I believe, but I cannot argue for that here.

9.   One reason someone might think they are necessary is if the explanatory gap problem is confused with a reduction of phenomenal states to brain states and one accepts the classical model of reduction one kind of entity to another. I think it is a mistake to view the explanatory gap problem as a reduction problem, regardless of the model of reduction. See chapter 6 for more on the issue of reduction in this context.

10.   In discussing this analogy earlier, my emphasis on the point that liquidity must be understood in its ordinary observational way rather than any physio-chemical sense of that term was to preserve the parallel between the first-person and third-person aspects that we find between subjective states and brain states.

11.   Galileo thinks he has resolved the problems associated with his view of the subjective qualities of four of the senses, but he has nothing substantive to say about sight and the attendant qualities of color and light, though he offers some inchoate speculations on the latter. One quaint aspect of his presentation, not presented here, is how he attempts to further ground each sense for the subjective qualities in the four basic elements of fire, air, earth, and water.

12.   Just as Berkeley did—see the section titled "Explaining the Appearance" in chapter 1. As we will see in chapter 6, Place and Smart failed in this respect.

13.   At one point, with regard to heat, Galileo explicitly states how his view is contrary to common sense: "From a common-sense point of view, to assert that that which moves a stone, piece of iron, or a stick is what heats it, seems like an extreme

vanity." (1623, p. 32) I will further discuss the common-sense view of secondary qualities and its relation to Galileo's view in chapter 6.

14.   True, the whole may function differently than the parts can individually but, for all that, the whole is not itself qualitatively different from its parts. Functionalists generally, though not without exception, admit their inability to reduce qualia, phenomenal states, to functional states. In chapter 2, I argued that they are also unsuccessful in reducing intentional states to functional states.

15.   Fred Dretske (e-mail, August 27, 2000) has objected to my claim that we need a new dynamics: " . . . the old dynamics provides everything you say the new (non-linear) dynamics provides. We take a gas, hydrogen, and burn it. The ash is water. Bingo, something completely new. So we are already familiar with the process in which you can take ingredients, combine them, and get something with an alto-gether new property (gas + gas = liquid)" I might add, in the spirit of his objection, that we do this utilizing the "old dynamics." What this objection misses is exactly similar to what David Chalmers' objection to my molecule/liquid analogy also missed. (For my response to Chalmers, see note 1.) It is at the ordinary observational level that an altogether new property occurs, (observed) gas + (observed) gas = (observed) liquid; observed liquids are certainly qualitatively rather different from observed gases. But, as in my response to Chalmers, at the physio-chemical level we do not get something new or radically different. $2H_2 + O_2$ molecules combine to yield $2H_2O$ molecules, molecules + molecules yield more molecules, albeit different molecules and with different strengths of inter-molecular bonds, but *qua* molecules and this micro level of explanation, *just more of the same.* So, Dretske's case shows nothing (radically) new and different when we restrict ourselves to considerations at the physio-chemical level, to the standard dynamics, to the "old dynamics." It is at the level of ordinary observation that the change from a gas to a liquid is radi-cally different. This difference in ordinary observations is not explained by an exclu-sive physio-chemical explanation at the micro level. The terms 'gas' and 'liquid' in the physio-chemical explanation have to do with differences in inter-molecular bonds, and as such, it is more of the same. It does not, without further ado, reflect on the ordinary observational (phenomenal) differences between that of "gas" and "liquid." (See my discussion regarding the ambiguity of such terms between our sci-entific and ordinary understanding of them in chapter 6.) At the physio-chemical level there is nothing substantially new. Similarly, as argued earlier, the molecule/liquidity case is only an analogy for the explanatory gap problem, when characterized in terms of inter-levels and when 'liquidity' is understood in its ordi-nary observational sense.

16.   Self-organization is a characteristic of chaotic systems. See the appendix to this chapter for a brief explanation of some central concepts of chaos theory.

17.   J. A. Scott Kelso (1997) lists among the conditions for a self-organized system that there must be a large number of elements with nonlinear interactions. He

points out that this requirement constitutes a major break with Sir Isaac Newton, whom he quotes as holding that "the motion of the whole is the sum of the motion of all the parts" (Definition II, *Principia*). In contrast, Kelso holds that "for us, the motion of the whole is not only greater than, but *different* than the sum of the motions of the parts, due to nonlinear interactions among the parts or between the parts and the environment" (16). Feedback models are sometimes thought to account for self-organized behavior. In counter to this, Kelso (9) appeals to the work of W. Ross Ashby, who proved feedback models are inadequate for complex systems with a large number of elements. He also argues that a feedback (linear) analysis is also precluded by the fact that there are no reference values with which the feedback may be compared.

18.   Detailed discussion of Freeman's work supporting the role of chaos in brain processing of information is found in the papers by Chris King, Carl Anderson and Arnold Mandell, Earl MacCormac, and David Alexander and Gordon Globus in MacCormac and Stamenov 1996b. Others have also successfully applied chaos theory to brain activity. For a fascinating and clear account of other successful applications of chaos theory to brain activity, see Kelso 1997.

19.   See, for example, Freeman 1996, 1991, 1992, and 1995—a sequence that goes, roughly, from simpler to more technical works.

20.   An issue here is related to what is known as the "binding problem." This problem is how the outputs from the different supposed feature detectors are connected. A proposed solution, one which Freeman, himself, had a hand in, is that the feature neurons fire synchronously (40 hertz). Freeman now rejects this as a pseudo-problem, for it is based on the idea of feature detector neurons in each of the sensory cortexes. Freeman rejects the idea of feature detector neurons because it is observer relative, and what is significant for the brain is the global activity of the neurons. Aside from the difficulties with feature detector neurons, the "40-hertz solution" is now rejected by him, since the frequency distribution in the visual and olfactory systems is not synchronized but broad spectrum, as Freeman has demonstrated. On the question of feature detectors, see the next note.

21.   Compare Akins' (1996) discussion of heat, where no single correlation is found between the heat stimulus and the various resultant changes in physiological states. The nonexistence of such correlations may well further indicate the need to examine more global properties of the brain through the use of chaos theory, as Freeman found in study of smell. I discuss Akins' work in chapter 5.

22.   A further fact that supports the contention that the system is chaotic is that the bulb and the olfactory cortex excite one another so that neither settles down, nor do they agree on a common frequency of oscillation. (If the connection is severed between the two, they become stable and quiet.) This competition between the two increases sensitivity and instability and contributes to chaos. The importance of this connection between the olfactory bulb and cortex when understood in the light

of another biological fact leads to a rather startling speculation. Here is, what I understand to be, the other biological fact. (I thank John Bickle for bringing this fact to my attention.) As the cortex increases in mass it takes on more functions, functions that in lower animal forms that have less cortical mass are performed by brain systems other than the cortex; this is particularly true of sensory systems. Suppose, in accordance with the mind/brain theory that I advance, which draws heavily upon the work of Freeman, that the *having* of phenomenal or contentful experience is a direct result of *one's own brain* undergoing a burst to a strange attractor, and that these burst states involve the cortex. Assuming that oscillations between the olfactory bulb and the olfactory cortex that occurs in humans does not occur in some lower animals whose cortex is not involved when their sense organs are appropriately stimulated, the speculation is that such lower animal forms *simply lack qualia, contentful states, or conscious states—they do not have subjective experiences.* In light of what I argue in the next chapter, such animals would be information bearers but not representers.

23.   If brain dynamics is chaotic then superficially, at least, this last feature would seem to go far in explaining why, although we can frequently give an ad hoc explanation of someone's behavior, we are not as successful in predicting what someone will do, despite *similar*, even empirically indistinguishable but not identical, initial conditions.

24.   This passage is clearer than it might otherwise have been if it were not for Ümit Yalçin's refusal to accept the idea that one could have a deterministic system whose states were not in principle predictable.

Chapter 5

1.   For an example of a violation of this stricture, see Macphail 1987. Macphail examines possible differences in intelligence from species to species without prior analysis of representation in humans. Vauclair (1990, p. 395) criticizes Macphail for not paying sufficient attention to the concept of representation. Vauclair takes a step in the right direction in offering a definition of representation. However, Vauclair does not go far enough, for he offers neither evidence nor argument that his concept of representation is that operative in the human performance of intelligent tasks.

2.   To the extent that I am right in maintaining the importance of the first-person perspective and the consequences I have drawn from it for an analysis of intentional states, I am also right in denying Dennett's claim that being able to take an "intentional stance" toward a system is sufficient for that system to have intentional states. The last claim requires further support in that Dennett (1987) would require, in addition to our being able to take an intentional stance toward a system, that the system itself exhibit a certain objective feature which he calls a 'real pattern', if the system is to have intentional states. (See e.g. Dennett 1987, pp. 25–26. For an

extended treatment of his idea of a real pattern, see Dennett 1991.) Consideration of whether talk of real patterns in this connection can avoid the problems the first-person perspective poses for Dennett's kind of analysis of intentional states will have to wait for another occasion, though my discussion of the distinction between representers and information bearers, below, independently supports the rejection of intentional stance type theories.

3.   The specific views examined are those of Churchland and Churchland (1983), developed further by Paul Churchland (1979), Fred Dretske (1985, 1995), and Ruth Millikan (1984, 1989).

4.   This is discussed further in the next section. See also Beckermann 1988.

5.   One anonymous referee who read the article version of this chapter did raise this objection.

6.   The reader is reminded that insisting on the conscious aspect of representations does not commit me to holding that when s is occurrently aware that r represents t, her awareness consists in her noticing some peculiar feature of either r or her occur-rent state. And that's a good thing, since if it did, that would seriously count against my view. See e.g. Kripke 1982, especially the latter portion of section 2, for a dis-cussion of why it is a mistake to look for such a feature. I am not sympathetic to views that associate a phenomenal aspect with intentional states for reasons already presented in chapter 3. Kripke's arguments here give further support for this rejec-tion. For an example of the contrary position, see Siewert 1998.

7.   Searle (1979) notes that Wittgenstein and Kenny have argued that an inten-tional state and its object have some "internal relation" to one another. Searle agrees and holds that an intentional state *is* internally related to its object: "Because an intentional state contains a representation we can now give a clear sense to the notion that it is 'internally related' to the object it represents: Any representation is internally related to its object in the sense that it could not be *that* representation if it did not have *that* object." (184) He realizes that much depends on how this rela-tion is explicated. My explication, given below, is in accord with this and is in terms of minimal content.

8.   Dretske and Millikan do not speak of "intrinsic representations," but they do attempt to eliminate indeterminacies regarding what is represented; so they do address in effect the particularity requirement. That they fail in this will be argued in a later section.

9.   Armstrong adds that not all concepts are selective capacities, and some non-simple concepts are selective capacities, but all simple concepts must have selective capacities.

10.   This is argued by Heil (1980). See especially pp. 164–167.

11.   If one is aware of the minimal content of one's thought then one is at least implicitly aware of a certain mapping. Alternatively, if one is aware of a particular mapping, one is also aware of a certain minimal content, the object of the thought as conceived by the agent. So whether we speak of mappings or objects here is a matter of convenience determined by the context.

12.   On my view, one can be a physicalist and still accommodate the first-person perspective. In the last section here, I indicate how the result may nevertheless be, in a worthwhile sense, objective. See also chapter 3.

13.   Indeed, the very idea of doing something for a purpose is one that presupposes the notion of representation in accordance with my (partial) analysis of representation, and as distinct from *information bearing*. This last concept and how it differs from representing will be explained below. A later section will examine in detail the failure of teleological theories of representation.

14.   The exact role conventions play in determining relevant mappings and just how an individual may deviate from those conventions is addressed in more detail in my discussion of Burge's thought experiment in chapter 7.

15.   Compare the section "Understanding, Explicating, and Individuating" in chapter 1. The reader is also reminded that on my theory, minimal content does not have ontological significance; it is merely a moniker for the subject of an agent's thought as she conceives it.

16.   We will see in chapter 8 that these results will have important consequences for Quine's Indeterminacy of Translation thesis.

17.   Compare my discussion of Dretske and Millikan below, where I charge that they do assume this claim.

18.   This is a standard notion of *information*. See, for example, Van Gulick 1990, p. 109. Nothing that I say turns on this exact formulation.

19.   In "object of attention" I mean both 'object' and 'attention' to be understood from a first-person perspective.

20.   In chapter 2 and in my 1996 paper, I argue that functionalism generally and Van Gulick's specific version of it (1988) fail to account for the special access we have to our own minimal contents. As to the inadequacy of teleological accounts of representation, see the section below titled "Clarification of the Scope of the Arguments."

21.   Nagel (1980, p. 161 and n. 5) makes similar points.

22.   On a more optimistic note: If it turns out that consciousness is necessary for representation, as I hold, it is not implausible to suppose that at some stage of scientific development we could objectively identify what feature enables consciousness in us. (For a hypothesis as to a candidate for the sort of brain state that is

promising in this regard, see Georgalis 2000 and chapter 4 of the present volume.) We would then be able to determine which non-human animals also have this feature and, therefore, assuming that certain other factors that are in play when we represent are similarly realized, have strong grounds to hold that they also have similar representational states.

23.   An advocate of an exclusive third-person methodology who holds this view is Ruth Millikan.

24.   Some variant of the appearance to which I refer is recognized and confronted by a number of authors. For example, even Dennett (1987), who wants a unified theory of all manner of representations, is concerned to explain the appearance of a difference in how we represent and how, say, thermostats do. He does so in terms of the kinds of connections to the environment and degree of complexity, to oversimplify a bit. Just how seriously Dennett takes the distinction is subject to interpretation, but that need not detain us. He revisits something like the distinction in "Real Patterns" (1991). Fred Dretske (1985, 1995) focuses on an item having meaning in a *system's cognitive economy* versus its being *assigned* meaning by us. I certainly do not mean to suggest that Dretske and Dennett draw the same distinction, or that mine is the same as either of theirs. Indeed, it is not. The point is simply that they recognize the need to address *some* such distinction. Whether they are successful in drawing the distinction in a principled way that can address the points I identify as crucial to my distinction is another matter. In a subsequent section I will argue that Dretske's and Millikan's manner of distinguishing information from representation are inadequate.

25.   Clearly, on my view information-bearing states are representational simply in a metaphorical way that is parasitic on the genuine sense. Compare Searle 1983, 1992. As is well known, Searle distinguishes intrinsic intentionality from both derivative and metaphorical intentionality. My debt to Searle on this and other matters is great.

26.   We can, for example, account for the mere appearance that the sun revolves around the Earth. What accounting for such appearances comes to is explained more fully in chapter 1 of the present work and in my 1990 and 1994 papers.

27.   A very early version of this section was presented in March 1993 at the University of Dayton at a colloquium on Recent Debates in the Cognitive Science Literature. Paul Churchland and Alvin Goldman were the invited speakers. I am grateful to both of them for their comments on my presentation and to the University of Dayton for the opportunity.

28.   The Churchlands make this move frequently. (In their 1983 paper, see the opening paragraph and passages on pp. 7–8, 11, and 14.) Such a move, in fact, turns on an equivocation between information-bearing creatures and ones that represent but, as I argue, it is a mistake to identify them.

29.   The Churchlands offer a somewhat more precise account of calibrational content: "A state S of a system O contains the calibrational content P if and only if O would not be in S unless P, with some high degree of probability n/m." (1983, p. 14). Paul Churchland develops this idea in his 1979 book.

30.   The Churchlands think that an advantage that calibrational content offers is that it provides for non-sentential models of content. Thus, it greatly expands the class of information bearers, as it admits as possibilities creatures who have no linguistic capabilities. This is as it should be. Having said that, I also point out that while a system need not bear information that is sentence-like, it does not follow that representation need not be sentence-like. For it does not follow that the information bearer has *any* representations, is ever in a representational state. Still, I am *not* arguing that representation *must be* sentence-like; rather I am pointing out that the Churchlands' argument to the contrary depends on the (mistaken) presupposition that an information bearer is, also, a representer. (The Churchlands also hold that an information-bearing creature is an epistemic one. But if I am right in arguing that there is a significant difference between information bearers and representers, then we should not be quick to agree with the identification of information bearing creatures with epistemic ones either.)

31.   Their apparently differing treatment of the shell creature example (as though hard-wired) from that of the snake (as if it had a genuine representational system), seems to conflict with this last result. The appearance of a difference in their evaluation of the two cases results primarily from the fact that in discussing the former they are concerned with exposing what they take to be a defect of the computationalist view, viz., its inability to provide a hookup between the representational system and the environment, a defect they maintain calibrational content corrects. I have argued that it corrects this problem only if calibrational content is identical to representation, but then their view is disabled from making the important distinction between representation and information bearing.

32.   Paul Churchland was in the audience when I presented a very early version of this section. He acknowledged my criticisms and the need to draw the distinction. He suggested that he could do so by bringing complexity considerations to bear. I am dubious that this can be done so as to avoid the criticisms I have raised. In any case, I am not aware of his having proposed any such account that goes beyond this general assertion. Note that "the complexity stratagem" that he suggests is similar to Dennett's (1987, 1991). Any such strategy must face the question why "more of the same" can yield something distinctly different. It is not enough to simply appeal to the evident greater complexity of systems that do represent, as it advances no understanding of how this could be. Compare the discussion of the gap problem in chapter 4.

33.   I am grateful to Reinaldo Elugardo for providing me with this way of formulating the issue.

34. Interestingly, the polarity of the magnetosome is different depending on whether the bacteria in which they reside are in the northern or southern hemisphere. If this were not so, the bacteria in one or the other hemisphere would have died off, since they would be pulled in the wrong direction, toward oxygen-rich water.

35. For example, for each number in the sequence 1, 2, 3, . . . , whenever I am not attending to it, I still have the unconscious belief that it is a natural number.

36. My debt to Searle is great, and I think he is profoundly right about intentionality. Still, I think he is wrong in holding that unconscious beliefs are intentionality, but abandoning this claim does not, I think, necessitate wholesale changes in his view.

37. In arguing for the connection principle, Searle (1992, pp. 156–162) advances his claim that unconscious beliefs have aspectual shape in some detail. He has confirmed in conversation that something like the short argument here presented captures the thrust of the point contained in the larger argument to the broader conclusion.

38. Since on my view there are no unconscious intentional states, the above would seem to totally undermine what Searle (1992, p. 156) calls the connection principle: " . . . all unconscious intentional states are in principle accessible to consciousness." My differences with Searle here are not as great as they may seem. I think there are two central points that Searle wants to advance with the connection principle. The first is that some, but not all, non-conscious states are importantly related to conscious states. The second is that all non-conscious states that are unconscious *mental* states are in principle accessible to consciousness. I am in complete agreement with the first; it is the point I attempt to capture with the unconscious/non-conscious distinction, which Searle used before me. I also accept a modified form of the second. Modified because I think that once we have a science of cognition (again, no matter whether it is based neuronally, computationally, or in some other way) it is highly implausible to think that *all* non-conscious states will be in principle accessible to consciousness though, undoubtedly, many will be. What their "accessibility" comes to on my view is that the structure and dynamics of the brain activity is such that given certain stimulations, it will undergo a burst to an attractor state, the latter is a manifestation of the conscious state and is qualitatively different from the preceding brain states. If this is so, it is misleading to speak of accessibility to the states that are prior to burst states. These states are designated as 'mental' because they lead to the relevant burst states but are not themselves accessible to consciousness. But as argued earlier, and as opposed to Searle, such unconscious mental states are not representational, not intentional. In contrast, those states that are *both* non-conscious *and* non-mental states do not lead to such bursts. (See chapter 4 and its appendix for further explanation of the role of burst states.) I cannot here discuss all of Searle's reasons for making the more general claim, but a

large part of why he is driven to do so is, I think, his holding that unconscious beliefs, *being beliefs*, must have aspectual shape. This, I have argued should be denied. Once denied, the connection principle must be reformulated, since there are no unconscious intentional states; still, if the two central points of the connection principle are as I have just stated, then the first and a modified form of the second is preserved. Thus, I claim that at least the spirit of the principle is preserved, even if Searle still wants more.

39. The aspectual shape of a mental state is determined by its representational nature. One might hold a belief under one representation, but disavow it under an extensionally equivalent representation.

40. Searle (1992, p. 158) thinks this because "we would still have to have some law like connection that would enable us to infer from our observations of the neural architecture and neuron firings that they were realizations [for example] of the desire for water not of the desire for H_2O."

41. For different reasons, I argued in chapter 3 that it is a mistake to approach intentionality, aboutness, on a perceptual model.

42. Compare my claim that we can give an objective account of subjective states, while utilizing, in part a first-person methodology. See chapter 3 and the next section.

43. However, Akins does say that "the distance between the neurophysiologist's view of sensory systems and our first-person perspective on conscious perception should raise a genuine puzzle . . . about representation" (1996, p. 367). Indeed it does, and I am pressing that puzzle as hard as I can.

44. Of course, if Freeman is right, this reply is a non-starter.

45. It is worth noting that insofar as the properties that Akins has called 'narcissistic' fail to correlate with distal properties, then they may not even count as information-bearing ones.

46. For a similar line, see Nagel (1980, pp. 162–164) on the contrast between objectivity and subjectivity, and on the importance of the first-person point of view in the study of human experience. See also Nagel 1986, pp. 32–37 and 60–66.

47. To the extent that one is abnormal, to that extent one's first-person perspective would be informative of others' subjective states that share the abnormality in question, assuming that certain other cognitive/rational faculties are in place.

Chapter 6

1. These results also have an affinity to some issues A. S. Eddington posed with his famous "two tables" and those that Wilfred Sellars raised when he contrasted what

he called the manifest and the scientific image. My theory provides the resources to better understand the issues they raised.

2. This is how Galileo characterized the common-sense position, which he rejected, as applied to the secondary qualities. See below.

3. Descartes distinguishes qualities we "suppose to be in objects" from "that which we experience in sensation." More specifically, he states that "we do not really know what it is that we are calling a colour, and we cannot find any intelligible resemblance between the colour which we suppose to be in objects and that which we experience in our sensations." These quotations are from the *Principles*, section 70, as reprinted in Rosenthal 1991b. Locke distinguishes "Ideas . . . as they are Ideas or Perceptions in our Minds; and as they are modifications of matter in Bodies that cause Perceptions in us." (This is from *Essay Concerning Human Understanding*, Book II, Chapter VII, as reprinted in Rosenthal 1991b.) Locke calls the former "Ideas," the latter "Qualities." In these passages, we have all but an explicit claim that 'color' is ambiguous between (1) and (2).

4. As David Hilbert does in *Color and Color Perception* (1987).

5. The latter is suggested by Fred Dretske (1996, p. 145) as a reason why some philosophers reject phenomenal externalism. Obviously the view presented here is in opposition to phenomenal externalism, but it does not depend on an act-object analysis of sensory experience.

6. In characterizing them as "starting points," I do not mean to subscribe to the view that they are somehow incorrigibly given, nor do I think that what I say commits me to that. I do hold that they are, at the very least, apparent facts that require an explanation and even an eliminativist regarding them has the obligation to explain why they appear to us as they do. Compare chapter 2, where I similarly talk of certain non-phenomenal data, and chapter 1, where I discuss what "explaining the appearance" comes to.

7. The "what it is like" aspect and how it is lacking in ordinary instruments was discussed in chapter 3, the radical differences in character that I mention was also discussed there and more fully in chapter 4.

8. There is, of course, a sense of 'real' that is independent of the perceiver. Clearly the subjective experiences are not real in this sense but, again, that point is already embedded, and granted, in the objective/subjective distinction, so *that* cannot be at issue here.

9. See chapter 4, where I present Galileo's account. I argue that, although it is rather successful in accounting for the degree of intensity of the qualitative feature, it fails in explaining the qualitative features themselves.

10. Recall from chapter 3 that no one would attempt to draw any negative ontological conclusions concerning the existence of voltmeter states based on the fact

that those states are similarly dependent on the voltmeter, and there is no good reason to draw such negative conclusions concerning our subjective states and their features.

11.   Galileo, as best I can tell, was never tempted to *identify* the secondary qualities with their objective external causes, as Hilbert and other contemporary writers do. He simply denied the reality of the subjective side *because* it is subjective.

12.   I am simplifying here, as the thermodynamical concept of heat preceded that of the kinetic theory. I will be more precise regarding these matters in the next section where such differences play a more consequential role.

13.   Recourse to a dictionary to determine the meaning of 'heat' is both amusing and interesting. It is amusing because the first definition of heat is "the quality of being hot" and the first definition of 'hot' is "having much heat" (and this from *Webster's Unabridged Dictionary*, second edition, 1979!). It is interesting because in the first definition of 'heat' after stating it is "the quality of being hot," it immediately continues as follows: "hotness: in physics, heat is considered a form of energy whose effect [what effect?] is produced by the accelerated vibration of molecules . . . "; this appears to conflate the subjective and objective sense of heat, unless one takes the "quality of being hot" objectively. A number of other definitions are offered, of particular note is definition 4 of heat as a sensation, which appears to conflate the objective and the subjective: "the sensation [subjective] produced by heat [objective]; the sensation experienced [subjective] when the [sentient] body is subjected to heat [objective] from any source." Some of the more metaphorical definitions of 'heat' are exclusively subjective. I take it that this is some support for my claim that the two senses are not clearly recognized as distinct.

14.   What exactly these features are is a nice question. I try to say something about this in chapters 3 and 4. We are aware of such features when our brains are in certain states, but it is the *having* of such brain states that is crucial and, importantly, this is additional to the brain states themselves.

15.   Others—for example, J. Barry Maund (1995)—also argue for the importance of the distinction between, as he puts it, "color-as-we-experience-it" and "the cause of color-as-we-experience-it." Christopher Peacocke (1983) distinguishes color qualia from colored things, holding that, say, a green quale and green grass are not "green" in the same sense. Colin McGinn (1996) wishes to develop a theory that respects the facts that color is both subjectively constituted and a feature of external objects. He holds contrary to his earlier view that a strictly dispositional theory of color does not adequately provide for the former, what he calls the "phenomenology of color perception." Though McGinn recognizes the importance of the subjective here, his account differs significantly from my own.

16.   This is granted, in a backhanded sort of way, by Michael Tye (1995, p. 170): "For the state must surely be thought of *as* a phenomenal state, *as* having a certain

phenomenal character, if it is to be *totally* understood. It follows that anyone who thought of the essence of the state solely in terms of its tracking certain external properties . . . would not fully understand it." I do not discuss his views in detail, though I think he fails to provide the required understanding; there is no improvement in this regard in his 2000 book.

17.   Larry Hardin read an earlier draft of this chapter and generously provided me with comments and criticisms. In particular, some of his remarks are what prompted me to introduce the distinction between f- reductions and t-reductions. His comments also resulted in the elimination of several pages and the correction of some errors from the earlier draft. I am most grateful to him for his constructive assistance.

18.   Though the term 'temperature' is now well entrenched in ordinary discourse, its association with a metric suggests that its entrenchment occurred well after that of 'heat' and after the scientific means were developed to measure it.

19.   I will discuss Place's and Smart's view in more detail below, and argue that recognizing the distinction does not circumvent serious objections to the identity theory, as they formulated it.

20.   I say 'modified' since at this point it is now understood that the felt heat is not an intrinsic property of an external body.

21.   Needless to say, a full defense of this requires that I deal with a number of well-known issues that are contrary to this claim, issues first raised by Hilary Putnam. To do so here would take us too far a field, however. I hope to deal with this more fully at a future time but some relevant points have already been presented in my discussion of Twin Earth in chapter 2.

22.   One thing Place and Smart thought important about the scientific identities they used as a model for sensation–brain processes identity is that they are contingent. The 'is' of composition rather than the 'is' of definition is the kind of identity at issue, and it provides the basis for the claim that the identity between sensations and brain processes is contingent. This in turn enabled them to avoid objections, which I do not rehearse here, based on the true claim that one could know sensations without knowing anything about brain processes.

23.   The same applies to the identities discussed in the previous section. For example, we do not "experience" heat and molecular motion in the same way. There are a number of complications as to just how one would characterize how we "experience" molecular motion; dealing with these complications would take us to far a field into issues in the philosophy of science (but see below regarding the observational/theoretical distinction). It is enough for the point I wish to make here that we simply notice that it clearly is different for the two cases. Compare what I say below regarding the analogous case of detecting electrical discharge.

24.   These are not normally distinguished (e.g., Question: "What is that (flash of light) in the sky?" Answer: "It is lightning.").

25.   Smart offers no candidate for what is the publicly observable lightning; he apparently expects us to just "get it." I do not, for the reasons indicated. This lacuna in Smart's discussion masks a confusion in his view and has contributed to the obscuring of the point that I am at pains to uncover.

26.   I offered such an explanation in chapter 4.

27.   It is this psychologically immediate projection that drives the false common-sense view, discussed earlier, that the experienced sensory feature is itself a feature of the external body. It is the "transparency of experience" that Gilbert Harman and Michael Tye make so much of.

28.   For Place, the "operations" for determining one's state of consciousness with regard to sensations is simply the attentive having of them, experiences. So my dropping the qualification of 'operation' in favor of just 'experiences' in statement (3) does not give reason for Place to reject (3).

29.   A similar point was made in objection to the perspectival view of subjectivity discussed in chapter 3.

30.   Louise Antony and Joe Levine made this point in conversation. Note, also, that if the identification of sensory experiences is made with states of the brain, rather than to features external to the body, then the objection presented does not apply. For the relevant brain states are certainly involved even in color dreams, though not necessarily in precisely the same way as they are when we experience color while awake. (Whether they are the same is an empirical question.) The objection is thus avoided given this identification. This is no solace to the objectivist, for the ground for the claim that external bodies (external to the perceiver) are themselves colored or hot is also lost, since the subjective feature is identical to a brain state of the perceiver and these are certainly not features of bodies external to the body of the perceiver. Indeed, objectivists who hold that our experiences represent (e.g. Lycan, Armstrong, and Tye) sometimes appear to vacillate on just what is represented, whether it is a brain state or a quality external to the body of the perceiver.

31.   David Rosenthal (1985) argues that colors of afterimages and of physical objects are not the same. (He does so by way of criticism of Jackson's argument that the identification of color with the light reflecting properties of bodies fails because after images have color but cannot reflect light.) This is another case of a dispute that is clarified once the ideas of minimal content and objective content are recognized. Both Jackson and Rosenthal have a point. Jackson is focusing on the minimal content, while Rosenthal is in effect identifying one sense of color with the minimal content and the other with the objective content. Rosenthal goes wrong, however, in that he fails to see that even when spectral reflectances are the cause of the color experience, the perceiver still has a minimal content that can be exactly like

what he has when he has an after image. So, Rosenthal is right in thinking that color is ambiguous, but he has misplaced the ambiguity.

32.   But see Hardin 1988 and 2004 for powerful arguments against this claim. The 1988 book contains a probing and deep discussion of a number of central philosophical issues concerning color. Much of my thought on color has been shaped by it.

33.   I hasten to add that, although I speak of the "qualitative content" and the "subjective referent" of color, I do not endorse, nor am I in any way committed to, a sense-data theory, or to any other theory that takes the qualitative character itself to be an object. All that is meant is that qualitative character itself can be, and is, a legitimate topic of discourse. What I have in mind is along the same lines as my earlier remarks on what are legitimate topics of discussion. Ned Block makes a similar point: " . . . the phenomenist need no[t] have any commitment to phenomenal individuals" (1996, p. 35). William Lycan (in Villanueva 1996) also makes a similar point: "A quale is, not the introspectable monadic qualitative property of an actual phenomenal individual (there being no such things), but that of *what seems to be* a phenomenal individual and is referred to, individuated and counted as such."

34.   Fred Dretske, Gilbert Harman, and William Lycan defend this position in several articles; see, for example, their papers in Villanueva 1996. John McDowell defends this view in his 1994 paper, and Michael Tye does so in his 1995 and 2000 books.

35.   Michael Tye is an objectivist who finds the idea of massive error in perception unsavory. He says that "to convict such experiences of massive error . . . is just not credible" (2000, p. 46). What support does he offer for this bold claim? Astonishingly, just a common-sense intuition: "It seems totally implausible to hold that visual experience is systematically misleading in this way." (ibid.) Having favored us with his intuition, he immediately assures us that "the qualities of which you are directly aware in focusing on the scene before your eyes and how things look are not qualities of your visual experience" (ibid.) Shall I say it? This is less than compelling.

Chapter 7

1.   Burge 1979. All page references to Burge in the present chapter are to this volume.

2.   This is reflected in Burge's willingness to call embedded that-clauses "content-clauses." We will see that Burge is not as careful as he ought to be in keeping that-clauses and mental contents distinct. A further factor contributing to the blurring of these is already present when Burge says that a that-clause '*provides* the content'. For reasons that will become clear, I prefer to say that it *expresses* the content.

3.   Here I would use the word 'express'. See the preceding note.

4. Saying this, of course, is not to deny that there is a complex interplay between a person's linguistic abilities and their beliefs. I will have more to say about this interplay in my discussion of "sophisticated notions" below.

5. I quote at length to provide the context for parts that I will discuss in this chapter: "We suppose that in the counterfactual case we cannot correctly ascribe any content clause containing an oblique occurrence of the term 'arthritis'. It is hard to see how the patient could have picked up the notion of arthritis. The word 'arthritis' in the counterfactual community does not mean *arthritis*. . . . We suppose that no other word in the patient's repertoire means *arthritis*. 'Arthritis', in the counterfactual situation, differs both in dictionary definition and in extension from 'arthritis' as we use it. Our ascriptions of content clauses to the patient (and ascriptions within his community) would not constitute attributions of the same contents we actually attribute. For counterpart expressions in the content clauses that are actually and counterfactually ascribable are not even extensionally equivalent. However we describe the patient's attitudes in the counterfactual situation, it will not be with a term or phrase extensionally equivalent with 'arthritis'." (79)

6. The number of other "background beliefs" required to have the target belief are extensive and varied, for example, that the subject of the experiment has a body. There is, however, no need to make these other background beliefs explicit in the discussion of the experiment, as they do not bear directly on any possible differences in content the subject might have actually and counterfactually. Although background belief (3) is not literally part of the content of the target belief, it is important in that it bears on how the agent's expresses his target belief. Apart from this, not much in this paper turns on the distinction between component and background beliefs, although I think there are important applications of it. There is some kinship between the very rough distinction as I have drawn it and the rather detailed account of a more general distinction between what Searle (1983) has called the Network and the (local) Background.

7. I will go further than Crane by arguing below that the *having* of a sophisticated notion *requires* linguistic capabilities; moreover, I will argue that these capabilities need to be actualized to carry out the experiment, and that this requires that the agent has various beliefs, such as (3), pertaining to the use of words in his community. I take it that Crane would be sympathetic to my claim that Bert has belief (3). However, unlike me, Crane adopts a reinterpretation strategy: he ultimately argues that the subject of the experiment has a true belief involving a different notion of *tharthritis* (1991, pp. 18–22). As I have already indicated, I do not think reinterpretation is the way to go. However, I do agree with Crane's conclusion that Burge's thought experiment does not establish that intentional states are broad, though my argument for this is clearly different. I also note that In the same essay Crane argues that Putnam's famous Twin-Earth thought experiment also fails to establish that intentional states are broad. He concludes from his discussion of Putnam and Burge that we do not need a notion of narrow content, for he maintains that its intro-

duction was simply a response to the worries they raise, and he thinks he has put such worries to rest. I too have argued, though differently, for the deflation of the Twin-Earth experiment (see chapter 2), and I am here doing the same for Burge's thought experiment. I obviously disagree, however, with Crane's further conclusion, namely, that once these experiments are dispensed with no notion of narrow content is needed (23–24). In chapter 1, I argued for a new kind of narrow content, *minimal content*, independent of Burge's and Putnam's thought experiments, that is necessary for an adequate account of intentionality and phenomenality. In chapter 2 and in the present chapter, I have pressed this concept into service to deflate both experiments. (For a discussion of Putnam's thought experiment, see chapter 2 above.)

8. The arguments of this chapter are mostly the same as those in my 1999 paper. Anthony Brueckner (2001) has challenged the sufficiency of (1)–(3) by offering a counterexample. In my 2003b paper, I argue that his challenge fails. My response to Brueckner is included in a separate section below.

9. Rod Bertolet commented on a much shorter version of this paper at a meeting of the Central States Philosophical Association (Mt. Pleasant, Michigan, 1995). He raised some extremely useful criticisms that greatly assisted me in making important clarifications and changes in the paper. I am deeply grateful to him for the criticisms.

10. As Burge himself has correctly argued (101), were the subject confronted with his deviation, he would not persist, insisting he meant something different, rather he would correct his word usage and, I would add, not insignificantly, his understanding of the notion associated with the word.

11. Although I agree with Burge that the patient's deviance does not force any reinterpretation of his notion, the difference between Burge and me on the formulation of this deviance is critical. Ultimately, it comes down to whether claims pertaining to deviance should be formulated as (1) the individual has "the same notion," in *some loose sense*, but is still a bit off, which is what I will argue for, or as (2) he has the *exact* same notion, and his deviance is due to errors in his understanding. The latter formulation requires a distinct—but untenable—demarcation between one's having or understanding a notion and relevant collateral information. I argue for this below.

12. But see the previous note and relevant text below as to the difficulty in formulating, in a neutral way, this deviance. This difficulty ensues because Burge and I locate the source of the deviance differently.

13. This is not unusual when translating from one language to another. In fact it is curious that in one of Burge's criticisms of a metalinguistic approach, he uses the case of a foreigner sharing a notion with us but lacking the term we use as *no* reason to deny that the foreigner shares our notion (96). Perhaps Burge is assuming

here that the foreigner has some *other* term in his own language whose dictionary definition and extension is equivalent to our own, as is frequently the case. My point is broader: even if the foreign language lacks any extensionally equivalent term, a native speaker of that language may still have a notion which coincides with one of ours, though his notion would then deviate some from his fellows. And, as I have just argued, if this were not possible, Burge's thought experiment cannot even get started.

14.   As with minimal contents, the first-person perspective is essential for the concept of individual notions, though that of community notion is wide. The latter wide concept bears a direct relation to meaning. Despite the fact that meaning is a wide concept, I will argue in chapter 8 that the first-person perspective plays a crucial role in determining *which* meaning is at issue. Keeping apart the concepts of *meaning* and *which meaning* is, we shall see, very important. Finally, the discussion in chapter 8 of how the first-person perspective is related to questions about meaning contributes to an understanding of how individuals' notions and meanings are related.

15.   My position does not deny that what notions one has is partly dependent on one's understanding of them: One cannot think that arthritis has nothing to do with either aches or joints and still be said to have the community notion of arthritis. See my discussion of the difference between understanding and individuating a content in chapter 1, as it bears on a related difference between Burge and me.

16.   Compare my thesis that thoughts are systematically ambiguous between a subjective and objective reading (chapter 1) and my discussion of Twin Earth (chapter 2).

17.   In chapter 2, I examine the complicated relations between the extension of a term, the extension for an agent, and the term's application by an agent, and I argue that neither different extensions nor different applications of terms imply different mental contents. These results are grounded on my concept of minimal content, argued for in chapter 1.

18.   In this article Brueckner discusses my 1999 paper. The present chapter includes all the material presented in that paper.

19.   Of course, if Brueckner's objections to the part of my argument he does address were sustainable, *and* if he were to show that they disable the rest of my argument, then there would be no need to fully deal with the remainder of my argument. But to show the latter conjunct he would, at the very least, have to recognize those parts of my argument that I will demonstrate he ignores.

20.   Brueckner quickly raises several "doubts" about my claim that (1)–(3) is necessary (388), but he elects to pass on these. He neither explicates nor supports these doubts, but I will comment on two of them. He wonders if (1)–(3) are necessary if the subject of the experiment spoke only German, but he fails to mention that I explicitly deal with just such a case (1999, pp. 149–150). Another doubt he raises

concerns my formulation of (1), which originally read "There is an ache in my thigh" (1999, p. 148); Brueckner thinks that it suggests that arthritis always aches. That this is so is not clear to me, but in any case, I have changed (1) to "Sometimes my thigh aches." This change has no repercussions for my argument.

21.   The issues dealt with include the following: • That mental contents or notions need not be linguistic; so creatures lacking language may still have mental notions. • That having a sophisticated notion, such as *arthritis*, does require linguistic ability, but it does not require that they be English speakers and that they have the word 'arthritis' in their vocabulary. As a result, (3) needs to be indexed to the language of the agent. • Whether my analysis is unduly epistemological. (It is not.) • Although (3) is part of my analysis of the target belief, my analysis is not metalinguistic in a way that would make it subject to any of Burge's many arguments against "meta-linguistic approaches."

22.   When I argued against Burge's widely accepted view in my 1999 paper, I hoped for responses but feared neglect. I did not expect to receive both in the same paper, as I did in Brueckner's.

Chapter 8

1.   I will typically indicate intended reference and interpretation as IR and II, not so much as to save space as to remind the reader that I wish these expressions to be understood in certain specific ways; I am not simply appealing to their vernacular meanings. Though what I say of them is not unrelated to the vernacular, it is narrower in scope.

2.   Hereafter, Quine's *Ontological Relativity and Other Essays* (Columbia University Press, 1969) will be cited as *OR*.

3.   The concepts of ideal agent, individual, and community notions were discussed in some detail in chapter 7.

4.   Of course there are exceptions. See Quine on suspending the homophonic rule of translation (1969, p. 46).

5.   To speak thus of the "usual purported denotation" we must assume that in fact we know what others' IRs are and they are the same as one's own; what grounds there are for making such an assumption and the extent to which admitting II (IR) leads to a privacy of language will be considered below.

6.   I assume, as I think Quine does, that the native is a standard or typical language user.

7.   Quine allows that expressions such as 'the speaker's intended reference' have some *practical* value; this reflects his attitude toward intentional idioms generally. See *WO*, p. 221.

8.   Compare my discussion of similar problems regarding the determination of another's minimal content in chapters 1 and 3.

9.   The reasoning here is similar to that which leads one to mistakenly think that one must move to a second-order thought to talk of self-consciousness; it results from applying a strictly third-person methodology where it is inappropriate. (See chapter 2.)

10.   We will see that Quine appears to make a similar move to the one I just made when he speaks of "taking words at face value." I will argue that this move cannot do the same work for him as it does for me because he restricts himself to a third-person methodology.

11.   Long ago Chisholm argued that terms such as 'meaning' and 'reference' can only be analyzed in terms of intentional idioms such as 'takes there to be', 'believe' and 'ascribe'. I take this view, though not directed overtly against Quine's, to be compatible with mine. In fact at the end of "Sentences about Believing" (1956) he sketches a position one might take against himself, one that sounds very Quinean, though not exclusively so. It is to the effect that intentional sentences are not factual; this is reflected in Quine, when he denies there is a correct answer as to which translation to attribute to a speaker, and that the inscrutability of reference, is not an inscrutability of a fact.

12.   See, e.g., p. 92 of Quine 1960 and pp. 6–11 of *OR*.

13.   This last point is complicated for a variety of reasons. One is that in the context of radical translation one is basically assuming that one's respondents are representative of their community, that their IRs match those of the communities, match the objective references of the terms.

14.   These roughly correspond to appealing to paraphrase and ostension, respectively, discussed above.

15.   None of the preceding should be construed as saying anything about ontic reference. To talk of the "usual denotations" of a term is to talk of the inter-subjective agreement on the kinds of objects that the speakers of the language *take there to be*, and it is not to say anything about what is "really" in the world (though some may wish to take this further step). When we speak of the objects we take there to be— the usual denotations of our referring terms—we are, of course, not merely speaking of stimulations, nor of phonemic or inscriptional types (formal languages). The stimulations are the signs or evidence for the objects that are purported to be in the world. At the level of the individual agent, this is the intended reference; where there is a presumption of identity across agents' intended references it is objective reference. Both of these are independent of ontic reference.

16.   Hereafter, *Word and Object* (Quine 1960) will be cited as *WO*.

17.   The propensity to underplay the semantic part can be seen in Quine's early article "Meaning in Linguistics" (in Quine 1961). Quine consigns the semantical

part of linguistics to lexicography where the focus is on synonymy and 'having meaning' or 'significant' rather than 'meaning'. He then goes on to locate the problem of significance with the grammarian whom he describes as cataloguing short forms and working out the laws of their concatenation resulting in the class of all significant sequences. Notice though that the result is the class of all syntactically significant sequences (short forms and their permissible concatenations), not semantic significance. In fairness, he does eventually acknowledge that the grammarian needs over and above formal construction a prior notion of significant sequence for the setting of his problem and Quine admits he thereby draws on the old notion of meaning. He nevertheless does not alter the notion of a significant sequence in his article and on considering what he has said in *OR* on knowing a word it would seem that he is still leaning toward the syntactic line. Why he would do so is clear; syntax is more likely to be behaviorally ascertainable, semantics beyond use, is not.

18. The latter conjunct does obtain if indeterminacy of translation applies to oneself, but this begs the question. For with II fully admitted, we do not have first person indeterminacy and then the second conjunct does not follow from the first.

19. Certain distinctions must be kept clear. The sense in which the alternatives are equivalent is the sense in which the method of stimulus classes cannot distinguish them. The alternatives are not equivalent in the sense that what the sentences *assert* on different manuals is the same. At least they are different from an ordinary point of view or once intended interpretation is admitted. The properties of, say, rabbits are quite different from the properties of rabbit stages. I accept that the alternatives are equivalent in the first sense without accepting that they are equivalent in the latter sense. More on this later.

20. If the alternatives were not genuinely different then what point would there be in intending one rather than another? The answer would seem to be that there is no point to it, and Quine would be right in rejecting the idea that some single manual is the correct one. But even this defense only works *provided* one *knows* the alternatives are equivalent. Thus, even granting the equivalence of alternatives, in some very strong sense, there would still be *some* point to maintaining a speaker intended one rather than another, provided she does not know they are equivalent. To maintain this in the situation envisioned would not lack significance. Thus, if I intend to be talking about enduring things and do *not know* that I could be equivalently, if it is equivalently, be talking about stages, then there is still some point to saying that I *intend* the one alternative and not the other. (We are here of course engaged with difficulties of substituting in opaque contexts: S intends a, and a is equivalent to b, though S does not know the latter, and hence, it is not the case that S intends b.) Independent of this, I argue that the alternatives are indeed different, but that aside, we still see that there is still some point to our talking of an individual intending one interpretation rather than another, even if the interpretations are equivalent, so long as the individual is ignorant of the equivalence. I do not put

much in this last argument, as Quine could with some plausibility respond that the ignorance supposed in the case reflects his point, made earlier, that the manuals seem different when parts are considered apart from the whole. I mention it primarily because I think the indicated connection of these issues to those surrounding opaque contexts my be of some interest.

21. As I said, this is a view of Quine's that goes back at least to his 1961 book (pp. 40–43) and is echoed in WO (pp. 78–79), where he applies this idea to individual sentences in general (excepting observation sentences, which I will discuss in the next chapter).

22. The latter locution is to be taken as a one-word observation sentence.

23. I.e. "the grand synthetic one" that the individual ones add up to.

24. It is interesting to compare Quine's demonstration of the inadequacy of a strictly third-person methodology to distinguish alternative translations with Dretske's demonstration of the inadequacy of that method to uncover consciousness, which I took note of in chapter 3. I accept their results but take them as a reductio of their positions.

25. Effectively Quine is appealing to a verificationist principle. Such an appeal is explicit on p. 80 of OR, and comes under the guise of naturalism in OR—see especially pp. 29–30. His use of it to deny that there is a correct answer considered below, occurs at p. 78, WO, pp. 46–47, OR and in his discussion of the protosyntactician and arithmetician, pp. 41–43, OR.

26. My argument here does not depend upon the correctness of the dynamical theory of conscious states presented earlier. The argument goes through with just the assumption that the semantic correlations are somehow realized in the bilinguals' brains, which Quine grants.

27. Note that determining the different brain states would be objective even in the narrow sense, relying on a strictly third-person methodology.

28. The quotation is from Dewey.

29. In the passage just quoted, Quine seamlessly moves from the claim that meaning is primarily a property of behavior to the claim that there are no meanings beyond what is implicit in people's dispositions to behave. Clearly, the latter does not follow from the former.

30. Compare also the discussion of objective knowledge of the subjective in chapter 3.

31. For convenience, I quote one of the relevant passages at length: "I have urged in defense of the behavioral philosophy of language, Dewey's, that the inscrutability of reference is not the inscrutability of fact; there is no fact of the matter. But if there really is no fact of the matter, then the inscrutability of reference can be

brought even closer to home than the neighbor's case; we can apply it to ourselves. If it is to make sense to say even of oneself that one is referring to rabbits and formulas and not to rabbit stages and Gödel numbers, then it should make sense equally to say it of someone else. After all, as Dewey stressed, there is no private language." (*OR*, p. 47) Of course, having just argued that it makes no sense to say it of our neighbor and barring a private language, Quine concludes it make no sense in our own case.

32. See Searle 1987. Searle and I agree that Quine illegitimately overlooks the first-person perspective. There are numerous other points of agreement between Searle and me regarding what is wrong with Quine's view; still, there are significant differences between us regarding the inscrutability of reference and, more generally, on the status and analysis of privileged access.

33. Quine 1970, p. 182.

34. Quine (1970, p. 182) takes a different tack: "When this kind of hint is available, should we say that the supposed multiplicity of choices was not in fact open after all? Or should we say that the choice is open but that we have found a practical consideration that will help us in choosing? The issue is palpably unreal. . . ." He must claim that "the issue is palpably unreal," for if he takes the first alternative—choice among the alternatives was not open—he looses the indeterminacy of translation; whereas, if he takes the second alternative, he would be allowing that there is some reason to consider one of the alternatives as "better" than others, even though not a one of them is contradicted by the method of stimulus classes. But for Quine, from a theoretical point of view, we can ask for no more than that the alternatives are not contradicted by the application of this method; so, he rejects the very significance of questions that do presume more: "The question whether . . . the foreigner *really* believes A or believes rather B is a question whose very significance I would put in doubt. This is what I am getting at in arguing the indeterminacy of translation." (1970, pp. 180–181) Indeed, as earlier quoted, he says: "we recognize that there are no meanings, nor likenesses, nor distinctions of meanings, beyond what are implicit in people's dispositions to overt behavior." (*OR*, p. 29)

Chapter 9

1. Quine qualifies the inscrutability of reference here as *behaviorally* inscrutable; this is a qualification he normally suppresses.

2. A similar and related point arose in my discussion of Twin Earth in chapter 2, where I argued that different extensions do not automatically imply different thought contents, for the subject of the thought content could be understood as either the minimal or objective content. See also my discussion of Burge in chapter 7.

3. Fodor (1994) criticized Quine's claim of the inscrutability of reference for different reasons than I do. I argued in my 2000b paper that Fodor's criticism fails.

4.   Quine explicitly holds that it makes no sense to say what there is apart from doing so in some background language (see also *OR*, p. 68), but there are many other instances.

5.   Of course, there is a trivial and uninformative way that we can do this: What is there? Everything."

6.   Quine maintains that a realist view of physics is quite compatible with his position. See Davidson and Hintikka 1969, particularly p. 294 but also p. 303. Those who have read Quine over the years are familiar with this recurring claim in many of his works.

7.   I am deeply grateful to Professor Quine for his correspondence with me over several years on early versions of the material in this and the next several sections. Subsequent notes will indicate some of the points on which we came to agree and some which we did not.

8.   "I must grant the point, near the end of your paper, that taking the sophisticated observation sentences holophrastically does not free . . . their dependence on theory." (letter to me, December 13, 1993) Quine makes this explicit on p. 163 of his 1996 paper.

9.   See pp. 9, 13, and 14 of *WO*. Also the idea of an *occasion sentence* as there presented (ibid., 35–40), though broader than that of a one-word observation sentence, includes it. (See also p. 95, where he speaks of an *undifferentiated occasion sentence*.) In these cases, he is dealing with a string of marks or a sequence of sounds treated as a whole and geared to stimulation, with no attempt at parsing or the assignment of objects to terms. On the other hand, Quine also treats observation sentences, even when parsed, as occasion sentences. (See, e.g., 1960, pp. 40–46; 1993, pp. 108–109.) However, that a parsed observation sentence can be an occasion sentence is essentially dependent on its parsed history, where certain collateral information or prior theoretical considerations are the basis for the connection between current stimulation and utterance or assent to the sentence at issue. Treating parsed observation sentences as occasion sentences is of a piece with the mistakes of merging sentences of what I will call below levels 1 and 3 (because each can be treated holophrastically) and holding that they are up to doing the same epistemic work. I argue that such occasion or level-3 sentences cannot do the same epistemic work as one-word observation sentences (level 1). This is because collateral or theoretical considerations are involved in level- 3 sentences. For epistemic purposes, the levels must be kept distinct.

10.   He later remarks that a number of problems pertaining to observation and its epistemic value can be avoided by focusing on observation sentences rather than observation terms, and "Neurath and Carnap were on the right track here, in focusing on protocol sentences. But terms predominated in Carnap's further writings" (1993, p. 110). Thus, we have Quine's own emphasis on the holophrastic rather than piecemeal construal of observation sentences.

11.   Quine, in response to this particular passage, wrote: "On the contrary. I have not seen your 'objection' as an objection. It was what I had happily intended all along." (letter to me, February 23, 1997). That he intends this I certainly will not dispute. That one can embrace this point and still claim that these observation sentences are common reference points for incommensurable theories and also serve to buttress a scientific realism is precisely what I argue cannot be done. The reader must decide whether I have succeeded.

12.   This example was also discussed in on pp. 11–12 of Quine 1960.

13.   An unexpected bonus for a Kuhnian emerges. Proto-observation sentences may serve to answer those critics of Kuhn who have argued that his incommensurability thesis is incompatible with his claim that such theories are competing. How, the objection goes, can we say the theories are competing if they are incommensurable? The answer to such a worry might be: We know the theories are in competition because the same range of proto-observation sentences is at issue. This is consistent with their being incommensurable, for the latter turns on the piecemeal treatment of the sentences.

14.   Insofar as primitive observation sentences do treat of external things, present impingements are not sufficient for them—given indeterminacy of translation. Proto-observation sentences do not treat of external things—they do not treat of things at all, not even sensations. As I understand it, that is precisely why present impingements are sufficient for them. Thus, proto-observation sentences are not affected by radical translation, unlike primitive observation sentences. Primitive observation sentences, in general, do presume a "theory," albeit a widely shared one. Of course, if the competing theories are not fundamental or global, they will agree on a huge number of assumptions and so, relative to *those* theories, no questions are begged when appeal to such observation sentences is made. In that case, however, we are not looking at any fundamental epistemic or ontological issue, and there is room to question the scientist further.

15.   In another earlier letter (in response to questions concerning similar points which I put to him in the spring of 1992), Quine states: "Where then is our objectivity? Just at the checkpoints where, thanks to psychological conditioning, neural inputs are linked to our conceptual scheme; namely, the observation sentences. The objectivity of science consists in prediction of observation." But is this enough objectivity to adjudicate between theories or secure scientific realism? I think not. They do, as Quine notes, serve as *negative* checkpoints (1993, p. 111), but they cannot yield positive answers to such questions. As already observed, empirically equivalent theories must make the same predictions of proto-observation sentences; this is a necessary condition of their empirical equivalence. So this much objectivity cannot decide between them. If we move to primitive or level-3 sentences, knowledge of the world is presupposed. So using these sentences would leave one open to the

very criticism which necessitated the pristine observation sentences of level 1. Compare my discussion above.

16.   Giving (3) this "linguistic" reading fits well with what Quine has said of onto-logical relativity more recently (1992b, pp. 51–52): ". . . I can now say what onto-logical relativity is relative to, more succinctly than I did in the lectures, paper, and book of that title. It is relative to a manual of translation. To say that 'gavagai' denotes rabbits is to opt for a manual of translation in which 'gavagai' is translated as 'rabbit', instead of opting for any of the alternative manuals."

17.   Of course, Carnap allowed that various pragmatic considerations may lead us to adopt or prefer one over another.

18.   In fact, Quine rejects Carnap's internal/external distinction (see, e.g., OR, pp. 52–53), so one must not take the parallel I draw here too literally.

19.   Both essays appear in *Ontological Relativity and Other Essays* (1969). For inter-esting twists on the idea of perceptual similarity, see Quine 1996, pp. 160–162.

20.   The various moves and their shortcomings are outlined in Carl Hempel's widely anthologized classic "Empiricist Criteria of Cognitive Significance: Problems and Changes" (1950/2001).

21.   To better see this, consider one who was not trained by someone in the know and who, by most improbable chance, uttered 'There-is-copper-in-it' when appro-priately stimulated. In such circumstances, the utterance would correctly be consid-ered a one-word observation sentence, but *it would bear no linguistic relation* to the phonetically or typographically similar English sentence. Any other sounds or marks would have served as well. That this particular sequence of sounds or marks was used would be a stupendous coincidence. For such a case to have any bearing on the issues at hand, theory must have intruded somewhere, even if it did not for the ignorant subject being conditioned. I thank Ümit Yalçın for raising the possibil-ity of someone being holophrastically conditioned to a level-3 sentence.

22.   To illustrate, consider the following sentences uttered under appropriate stim-ulatory conditions: "There is a cup on the desk." "There is a jet passing overhead." (as when one witnesses a stream of smoke in the sky, but not directly the jet) "There is a mass spectrometer on the desk." "There is copper in it." (as in the discussion of the chemistry example of level 3). All these are quickly decidable by anyone having the relevant knowledge and presented with the appropriate stimulatory conditions; they are all, we may allow, observation sentences. There is also some reason to main-tain that as we move from the first to the last, these sentences become increasingly theory laden. The community of normal speakers of the language to which these are observational becomes ever slightly smaller as we move down the list. So the first has a higher degree of observationality to it than does the last.

23.   Just what gives rise to degrees of observationality in Quine is complicated. On p. 110 of the 1993 paper it is their theory-ladenness, their piecemeal treatment, that brings about the degrees of observationality, as it was for the positivists. But on pp. 108–109 Quine states that the degrees of observationality are attributable to two additional factors: how quickly is the quickly decidable sentence decided and whether it is corrigible. These factors, no doubt, are related to the sentences being treated in a piecemeal fashion, but they are additional. Put these complications aside. As we will presently see, these complications take a somewhat new twist in Quine's 1996 paper.

24.   These reflections were prompted by a letter from Lars Bergstrom. In addition, in a letter to me (February 20, 1996), he reports that "the degrees of observationality are rescinded in 'Progress [On Two Fronts']."

References

Akins, K. 1996. Of Sensory Systems and the "Aboutness" of Mental States. *Journal of Philosophy* 93: 337–372.

Alexander, D. M., and G. G. Globus. 1996. Edge-of-Chaos Dynamics in Recursively Organized Neural Systems. In *Fractals of Brain, Fractals of Mind*, ed. E. MacCormac and M. Stamenov. John Benjamins.

Anderson, C. M., and A. J. Mandell. 1996. Fractal Time and the Foundations of Consciousness: Vertical Convergence of 1/f Phenomena from Ion Channels to Behavioral States. In *Fractals of Brain, Fractals of Mind*, ed. E. MacCormac and M. Stamenov. John Benjamins.

Armstrong, D. M. 1963. "Is Introspective Knowledge Incorrigible?" *Philosophical Review* 72, no. 4: 417–432. Reprinted in *The Nature of Mind*, ed. D. Rosenthal (Oxford University Press, 1991).

Armstrong, D. M. 1968. *A Materialist Theory of the Mind*. Humanities Press.

Armstrong, D. M. 1973. *Belief, Truth, and Knowledge*. Cambridge University Press.

Beckermann, A. 1988. Why Tropistic Systems Are Not Genuine Intentional Systems. *Erkenntnis* 29: 125–142.

Benacerraf, P. 1965. What Numbers Could Not Be. *Philosophical Review* 74: 47–73. Reprinted in *Philosophy of Mathematics: Selected Readings*, second edition, ed. P. Benacerraf and H. Putnam. Cambridge University Press, 1983.

Block, N. 1978. Troubles with Functionalism. In *Perception and Cognition: Issues in the Foundation of Psychology*, ed. C. Savage. University of Minnesota Press.

Block, N. 1986. Advertisement for a Semantics for Psychology. In *Midwest Studies in the Philosophy of Mind*, no. 10, ed. P. French et al. University of Minnesota Press.

Block, N. 1996. Mental Paint and Mental Latex. In *Perception*, ed. E. Villanueva. Ridgeview.

Brueckner, A. 2001. Defending Burge's Thought Experiment. *Erkenntnis* 55: 387–391.

Burge, T. 1979. Individualism and the Mental. In *Midwest Studies in Philosophy*, volume 4, ed. P. French et al. University of Minnesota Press.

Burge, T. 1988. Individualism and Self-Knowledge. *Journal of Philosophy* 85: no. 5: 258–269.

Burge, T. 1992. Philosophy of Language and Mind: 1950–1990. *Philosophical Review* 101: 3–51.

Burge, T. 1997. Two Kinds of Consciousness. In *The Nature of Consciousness*, ed. N. Block et al. MIT Press.

Carnap, R. 1956. Empiricism, Semantics, and Ontology. In *Meaning and Necessity*, enlarged edition. University of Chicago Press.

Chalmers, D. 1996. *The Conscious Mind: In Search of a Fundamental Theory*. Oxford University Press.

Chalmers, D. 2002, ed. *The Philosophy of Mind*. Oxford University Press.

Chisholm, R. 1956. Sentences about Believing. In *Minnesota Studies in the Philosophy of Science*, vol. 2, ed. H. Feigl and M. Scriven. University of Minnesota Press.

Chisholm, R. 1976. *Person and Object*. Allen and Unwin.

Churchland, P. M. 1979. *Scientific Realism and the Plasticity of Mind*. Cambridge University Press.

Churchland, P. S. 1986. *Neurophilosophy: Toward a Unified Theory of Mind/Brain*. MIT Press.

Churchland, P. S. 1996. The Hornswoggle Problem. www.merlin.com.au/brain_proj/psch_2.htm.

Churchland, P. S., and P. M. Churchland. 1983. Stalking the Wild Epistemic Engine. *Nous* 17: 5–18.

Churchland, P. S., and P. M. Churchland. 1998. *On the Contrary: Critical Essays, 1987–1997*. MIT Press.

Crane, T. 1991. All the Differences in the World. *Philosophical Quarterly* 41: 1–25.

Crane, T. 2001. *Elements of Mind*. Oxford University Press

Crane, T. 2003. The Intentional Structure of Consciousness. In *Consciousness*, ed. Q. Smith and A. Jokic. Oxford University Press.

Davidson, D., and Jaakko Hintikka, eds. 1969. *Words and Objections: Essays on the Work of W. V. Quine*. Reidel.

Davidson, D. 1984. First Person Authority. *Dialectia* 38: 101–111.

Davidson, D. 1987. Knowing One's Own Mind. *Proceedings and Addresses of the APA* 60: 441–458.

Davidson, D. 1988. Reply to Burge. *Journal of Philosophy* 85: 664–665.

Davies, M., and G. W. Humphreys, eds. 1993. *Consciousness*. Blackwell.

Dennett, D. 1978. A Cure for the Common Code? *Brainstorms*. MIT Press.

Dennett, D. 1987. True Believers. In Dennett, *The Intentional Stance*. MIT Press.

Dennett, D. 1991. Real Patterns. *Journal of Philosophy* 88, no. 1: 27–51.

Dretske, F. I. 1985. Machines and the Mental. *Proceedings and Addresses of the American Philosophical Association* 59: 23–33.

Dretske, F. I. 1996. Phenomenal Externalism. In *Perception*, ed. E. Villanueva. Ridgeview.

Dretske, F. I. 1997. *Naturalizing the Mind*. MIT Press.

Dretske, F. I. 2003. "How Do You Know You're Not a Zombie?" In *Privileged Access*, ed. B. Gertle. Ashgate.

Eckhorn, R., R. Bauer, W. Jordan, M. Brosch, W. Kruse, M. Munk, and H. Reitboeck. 1988. Coherent Oscillations: A Mechanism of Feature Linking in Visual Cortex? *Biological Cybernetics* 60: 121–130.

Fodor, J. 1986. Why Paramecia Don't Have Mental Representations. In *Midwest Studies in Philosophy*, volume 10, ed. P. French et al.. University of Minnesota Press.

Fodor, J. 1988. *Psychosemantics: The Problem of Meaning in the Philosophy of Mind*. MIT Press.

Fodor, J. 1994. *The Elm and the Expert*. MIT Press.

Freeman, W. J. 1991. The Physiology of Perception. *Scientific American* 264, no. 2: 78–85.

Freeman, W. J. 1992. Tutorial on Neurobiology: From Single Neurons to Brain Chaos. *International Journal of Bifurcation and Chaos* 2, no. 3: 451–482.

Freeman, W. J. 1995. *Societies of Brains: A Study in the Neuroscience of Love and Hate*. Erlbaum.

Freeman, W. J. 1996. Interview with Jean Burns: Societies of Brains. *Journal of Consciousness Studies* 3, no. 2: 172–180.

Freeman, W. J., and K. Maurer. 1989. Advances in Brain Theory Give New Directions to the Use of the Technologies of Brain Mapping in Behavioral Studies. In *Proceedings, Conference on Topographic Brain Mapping*, ed. K. Maurer. Springer-Verlag.

Freeman, W. J., and B. Van Dijk. 1987. Spatial Patterns of Visual Cortical Fast EEG during Conditioned Reflex in a Rhesus Monkey. *Brain Research* 422: 267–276.

Galileo Galilei. 1623. *The Assayer*. Reprinted in part as "Two Kinds of Properties" in *Philosophy of Science*, ed. A. Danto and S. Morgenbesser (Meridian, 1960).

Georgalis, N. 1974. Indeterminacy of Translation and Intended Interpretation. Ph.D. dissertation, University of Chicago.

Georgalis, N. 1986. Intentionality and Representation. *International Studies in Philosophy* 18: 45–58.

Georgalis, N. 1990 No Access for the Externalist. *Mind* 99: 101–108.

Georgalis, N. 1994. Asymmetry of Access to Intentional States. *Erkenntnis* 40: 85–11.

Georgalis, N. 1995. Review: *The Nature of True Minds*. *Philosophical Psychology* 8, no. 2: 189–193.

Georgalis, N. 1996. Awareness, Understanding, and Functionalism. *Erkenntnis* 44: 225–256.

Georgalis, N. 1999. Rethinking Burge's Thought Experiment. *Synthese* 118: 145–164.

Georgalis, N. 2000a. Minds, Brains, and Chaos. In *The Cauldron of Consciousness*, ed. R. Ellis and N. Newton. John Benjamins.

Georgalis, N. 2000b. Reference Remains Inscrutable. *Pacific Philosophical Quarterly* 81, no. 2: 123–130.

Georgalis, N. 2003a. The Fiction of Phenomenal Intentionality. *Consciousness and Emotion* 4: 243–256.

Georgalis, N. 2003b. Burge's Thought Experiment: Still in Need of a Defense. *Erkenntnis* 58: 267–273.

Georgalis, N. 2006. Representation and the First-Person Perspective. *Synthese* 149: 3.

Gray, C., P. Koenig, K. A. Engel, and W. Singer. 1989. Oscillatory Responses in Cat Visual Cortex Exhibit Intercolumnar Synchronization Which Reflects Global Stimulus Properties. *Nature* 338: 334–337.

Hardin, C. L. 1988. *Color for Philosophers: Unweaving the Rainbow*. Hackett.

Hardin, C. L. 2004. A Green Thought in a Green Shade. *Harvard Review of Philosophy* 12: 29–39.

Harman, G. 1990. The Intrinsic Quality of Experience. In *Philosophical Perspectives*, volume 4: *Action Theory and Philosophy of Mind*, ed. J. Tomberlin. Ridgeview.

Heil, J. 1980. Cognition and Representation. *Australasian Journal of Philosophy* 58, no. 2: 159–168.

Heil, J. 1988. Privileged Access. *Mind* 97: 238–251.

Heil, J. 1992. *The Nature of True Minds.* Cambridge University Press.

Heil, J. 1998. Supervenience Deconstructed. *European Journal of Philosophy* 6, no. 2: 146–155.

Hempel, C. G. 1950. Empiricist Criteria of Cognitive Significance: Problems and Changes. Reprinted in *The Philosophy of Language*, ed. A. Martinich (Oxford University Press, 2001).

Hilbert, D. 1987. *Color and Color Perception: A Study in Anthropocentric Realism.* Center for the Study of Language and Information.

Horgan, T., and Tienson, J. 2002. The Intentionality of Phenomenology and the Phenomenology of Intentionality. In *The Philosophy of Mind*, ed. D. Chalmers. Oxford University Press.

Jackson, F. 1986. What Mary Didn't Know. *Journal of Philosophy* 83: 291–295.

Kitcher, P. 1993. Function and Design. In *Midwest Studies in Philosophy*, volume 18, ed P. French et al. University of Notre Dame Press.

Kripke, S. 1982. *Wittgenstein on Rules and Private Language.* Harvard University Press.

Kelso, J. A. S. 1997. *Dynamical Patterns.* MIT Press.

King, C. 1996. Fractal Neurodynamics and Quantum Chaos: Resolving the Mind-Brain Paradox through Novel Biophysics. In *Fractals of Brain, Fractals of Mind*, ed. E. MacCormac and M. Stamenov. John Benjamins.

Levine, J. 1983. Materialism and Qualia: The Explanatory Gap. *Pacific Philosophical Quarterly* 64: 354–361.

Lewis, D. 1988. What Experience Teaches. In *Mind and Cognition*, ed. W. Lycan. Blackwell.

Loar, B. 1988. Social Content and Psychological Content. In *Thought and Content*, ed. R. Grimm and D. Merrill. University of Arizona Press. Reprinted in *The Nature of Mind*, ed. D. Rosenthal (Oxford University Press, 1991).

Lycan, W. G. 1987. Phenomenal Objects: A Backhanded Defense. In *Philosophical Perspectives*, volume 1: *Metaphysics*, ed. J. Tomberlin. Ridgeview.

Lycan, W. G. 1996. *Consciousness and Experience.* MIT Press.

Lycan, W. G. 1999. The Plurality of Consciousness. Reprinted in *Proceedings of the Sixth International Colloquium on Cognitive Science*, ed. J. Larrazabal and L. Perez Miranda (Kluwer, 2004).

Lycan, W. G. 2001. The Case for Phenomenal Externalism. *Philosophical Perspectives* 15: 17–35.

Lycan, W. G. 2003. Perspectual Representation and the Knowledge Argument. In *Consciousness*, ed. Q. Smith and A. Jokic. Oxford University Press.

MacCormac, E. 1996a. Fractal Thinking: Self-Organizing Brain Processing. In *Fractals of Brain, Fractals of Mind*, ed. E. MacCormac and M. Stamenov. John Benjamins.

MacCormac, E., and M. Stamenov, eds. 1996b. *Fractals of Brain, Fractals of Mind*. John Benjamins.

Macphail, E. M. 1987. The Comparative Psychology of Intelligence. *Behavioral and Brain Sciences* 10: 645–695.

Macphail, E. M. 1990. *Behavioral and Brain Sciences* 13: 391–398.

Martinich, A. P., ed. 1990. *The Philosophy of Language*, second edition. Oxford University Press.

Maund, J. B. 1995. *Colours: Their Nature and Representation*. Cambridge University Press.

McDowell, J. 1994. The Content of Perceptual Experience. *Philosophical Quarterly* 44, no. 175: 139–153.

McGeer, V. 1996. Is "Self-Knowledge" an Empirical Problem? Renegotiating the Space of Philosophical Explanation. *Journal of Philosophy* 93: 483–515.

McGinn, C. 1989. Can We Solve the Mind-Body Problem? *Mind* 98: 349–366.

McGinn, C. 1996. Another Look at Color. *Journal of Philosophy* 93, no. 11: 537–553.

Millikan, R. 1984. *Language, Thought, and Other Biological Categories: New Foundations for Realism*. MIT Press.

Millikan, R. 1989. Biosemantics. *Journal of Philosophy* 86, no. 6: 281–297.

Nagel, E. 1961. *The Structure of Science*. Harcourt, Brace & World.

Nagel, T. 1980. What Is It Like to Be a Bat? In *Readings in Philosophy of Psychology*, volume 1, ed. N. Block. Harvard University Press.

Nagel, T. 1986. *The View from Nowhere*. Oxford University Press.

Nemirow, L. 1990. Physicalism and the Cognitive Role of Acquaintance. In *Mind and Cognition*, ed. W. Lycan. Blackwell.

Peacocke, C. 1983. *Sense and Content*. Oxford University Press.

Pitt, D. 2004. The Phenomenology of Cognition. *Philosophy and Phenomenological Research* 69, no. 1: 1–36.

Place, U. T. 1956. Is Consciousness a Brain Process? *British Journal of Psychology* 47: 44–50. Reprinted in *The Place of Mind*, ed. B. Cooney (Wadsworth, 2000).

Putnam, H. 1975. The Meaning of 'Meaning'. In Putnam, *Mind, Language, and Reality*. Cambridge University Press.

Pylyshyn, Z. 1980. The Causal Powers of Machines. *Behavioral and Brain Sciences* 3: 443.

Pylyshyn, Z. 1986. *Computation and Cognition*. MIT Press.

Quine, W. V. 1960. *Word and Object*. MIT Press.

Quine, W. V. 1961. *From a Logical Point of View*, second edition. Harper.

Quine, W. V. 1966. On Carnap's Views on Ontology. In *The Ways of Paradox and Other Essays*. Random House.

Quine, W. V. 1969. Ontological Relativity. In *Ontological Relativity and Other Essays*. Columbia University Press.

Quine, W. V. 1970. On the Reasons for the Indeterminacy of Translation. *Journal of Philosophy* 67, no. 6: 178–183.

Quine, W. V. 1992a. Structure and Nature. *Journal of Philosophy* 89: 5–9.

Quine, W. V. 1992b. *Pursuit of Truth*, revised edition. Harvard University Press.

Quine, W. V. 1993. In Praise of Observation Sentences. *Journal of Philosophy* 90: 107–117.

Quine, W. V. 1994. Promoting Extensionality. *Synthese* 98, no. 1: 143–151.

Quine, W. V. 1996. Progress on Two Fronts. *Journal of Philosophy* 93: 159–163.

Rey, G. 1998. A Narrow Representationalist Account of Qualitative Experience. *Philosophical Perspectives* 12: 435–458.

Resnik, M. D. 1981. Mathematics as a Science of Patterns: Ontology and Reference. *Nous* 15: 529–550.

Rosenthal, D. 1985. Review of Frank Jackson, *Perception: A Representative Theory*. *Journal of Philosophy* 82, no. 1: 28–41.

Rosenthal, D. 1986. Two Concepts of Consciousness. *Philosophical Studies* 49: 3: 329–359. Reprinted in Rosenthal, *The Nature of Mind* (Oxford University Press, 1991).

Rosenthal, D. 1990. On Being Accessible to Consciousness. *Behavioral and Brain Sciences* 13, no. 4: 621–622.

Rosenthal, D. 1991a. The Independence of Consciousness and Sensory Quality. In *Consciousness: Philosophical Issues*, volume 1, ed. E. Villanueva. Ridgeview.

Rosenthal, D. 1991b. *The Nature of Mind*. Oxford University Press.

Rosenthal, D. 1997. A Theory of Consciousness. In *The Nature of Consciousness*, ed. N. Block et al. MIT Press.

Rota, G., Sharp, D., and Sokolowski, R. 1989. Syntax, Semantics, and the Problem of the Identity of Mathematical Objects. *Philosophy of Science* 55: 376–386.

Schippers, B. 1990. Spatial Patterns of High-Frequency Visual Cortical Activity during Conditioned Reflex in Man. Master's thesis, University of Amsterdam.

Searle, J. R. 1958. Proper Names. *Mind* 67: 166–173.

Searle, J. R. 1979. Intentionality and the Use of Language. In *Meaning and Use*, ed. A. Margalit. Reidel.

Searle, J. R. 1980. Minds, Brains and Programs. *Behavioral and Brain Sciences* 3: 417–424.

Searle, J. R. 1983. *Intentionality*. Cambridge University Press.

Searle, J. R. 1984. Intentionality and Its Place in Nature. *Synthese* 61: 3–16.

Searle J. R. 1987. Indeterminacy, Empiricism, and the First Person. *Journal of Philosophy* 84, no. 3: 123–147.

Searle, J. R. 1992. *The Rediscovery of the Mind*. MIT Press.

Searle, J. R. 1995. *The Construction of Social Reality*. Free Press.

Shoemaker, S. 1990a. Qualities and Qualia: What's in the Mind? *Philosophy and Phenomenological Research* Suppl. 50: 109–131.

Shoemaker, S. 1990b. First-Person Access. In *Philosophical Perspectives*, volume 4: *Action Theory and Philosophy of Mind*, ed. J. Tomberlin. Ridgeview.

Shoemaker, S. 1994. Phenomenal Character. *Nous* 28: 21–38.

Shoemaker, S. 2001. Introspection and Phenomenal Character. *Philosophical Topics*. Reprinted in *The Philosophy of Mind*, ed. D. Chalmers (Oxford University Press, 2002).

Siewert, C. P. 1998. *The Significance of Consciousness*. Princeton University Press.

Skarda, C. 1987. Explaining Behavior: Bringing the Brain Back In. *Inquiry* 29: 187–202.

Smart, J. J. C. 1959. Sensations and Brain Processes. *Philosophical Review* 68: 141–156. Reprinted in *The Place of Mind*, ed. B. Cooney. Wadsworth, 2000.

Strawson, G. 1994. *Mental Reality*, MIT Press.

Tye, M. 1995. *Ten Problems of Consciousness*. MIT Press.

Tye, M. 2000. *Consciousness, Color and Content*. MIT Press.

Van Gulick, R. 1988. A Functionalist Plea for Self-Consciousness. *Philosophical Review* 97: 149–181.

Van Gulick, R. 1989. What Difference Does Consciousness Make? *Philosophical Topics* 17: 211–230.

Van Gulick, R. 1990. Functionalism, Information and Content. In *Mind and Cognition*, ed. W. Lycan. Blackwell.

Van Gulick, R. 1993. Understanding the Phenomenal Mind: Are We All Just Armadillos? In *Consciousness: Psychological and Philosophical Essays*, ed. M. Davies and G. Humphreys. Blackwell.

Vauclair, J. 1990. Wanted: Cognition. *Behavioral and Brain Sciences* 13: 393–394.

Villanueva, E., ed. 1996. *Perception*. Ridgeview.

Yalçin, Ü. 2001. Solutions and Dissolutions of the Underdetermination Problem. *Nous* 35, no. 3: 394–418.

Index